Ring of Freedom

RING of FREEDOM

Don Kesterson

ISBN-13: 978-0-9984707-4-0

LCCN: 2019915633

Cover design: Jay Johnson, Rock Graphics, Inc.

Typesetting: Eric Fritzius, MrHerman.com

Dedication

This memoir is dedicated to the efforts of the Vuong Family to escape communist Vietnam and seek freedom in the United States.

Contents

Other novels by Don Kesterson:

The President's Gold

Gold of the Spirits

Pawns: Magic Bullet

Pawns: Kings in Check

Find links to these at

www.DonKesterson.com

Introduction

The details of Dr. Vuong Tu Toan's 1980 escape from Vietnam come from the journal he kept as events were unfolding and from interviews with the Vuong family. Dr. Vuong, or Toan as he is referred to throughout, was a well-respected doctor living with his family in South Vietnam, one of those blessed individuals who loved helping people, treating the sick and making them better. Before the fall of South Vietnam, he and his family had a wonderful life in a little town near Saigon, mostly untouched by the war. He had married Nha-Y, the daughter of a judge for the South Vietnamese Army. At the time they began their multiple escape attempts, they had five children, the oldest of whom was thirteen years old, while the youngest had just turned two.

To appreciate the gravity of their escape, it is important to understand the historical background against which it unfolded. This introduction lays out the circumstances—for those readers who are not familiar with them—of the political and social situation after the fall of the South and during the construction of the Socialist Republic of Vietnam.

At the beginning of the 1970s, with the Vietnam Conflict still raging, South Vietnam was on the brink of collapse. The small country's eventual fate had probably been determined long before the conflict itself. During and after World War II, Indochina was in tumoil. Her borders shifted often, and several other countries, including France, China, and the United States, vied for influence over the country and the region. In 1954, the French and the Vietnamese convened a Peace Conference in Geneva, with representatives from France, northern and southern Vietnam, and delegations from both the United States and Communist China in attendance. Zhou En-lai, the leader of the Chinese delegation, encouraged the division of Vietnam to attempt to check the burgeoning power of Vietnam. This also enabled the Chinese to increase their power and influence in the region.

The division of Vietnam, the North communist and the South ostensibly democratic, caused an immediate migration of many thousands of people. Those who wanted to live under democratic rule went south and many—but not all—who remained loyal to Ho Chi Minh and the Viet Minh (later called the Viet Cong) went north. It has been estimated that several hundred thousand Viet Minh remained in South Vietnam. Ho Chi Minh had become the popular figurative head of North Vietnam due to his role in fighting the Japanese and the French. Ho was a close ally of the Soviet Union and Stalin, but not Communist China and Mao; however, he was politically savvy enough to maintain ties with Communist China. The southern portion of Vietnam was hard pressed to find a leader with the charisma of Ho, but ultimately, chose a warlord from northern South Vietnam, Ngo Dinh Diem; Diem was an ally of the United States. The lines were drawn—Between North and South Vietnam, between communism and democracy.

In the early 1970s, after the United States announced that they would begin to pull out of Vietnam, Zhou En-lai, Mao's top diplomat, went to Mao to persuade him to seek a détente with the United States. China had supported North Vietnam throughout the Vietnam Conflict, despite North Vietnam's stronger connection to Soviet Union. Mao and the Chinese Communist Party could not let either the United States or the Soviet Union gain a greater influence on their doorstep.

On February 21, 1972, Nixon and Kissinger arrived in China on a diplomatic mission. During the visit, Nixon and Chinese Premier Zhou En-lai agreed to increase contacts between their two countries; this proved a turning point in the relationship between Communist China and the United States. With the United States military completing their withdrawal of ground troops in South Vietnam in September 1974, the U.S. Congress struck another serious blow by only appropriating $700 million for South Vietnam. This left South Vietnamese military underfunded, lowering readiness and morale.

In October, 1974, sensing the kill, the North Vietnam Politburo started formulating a plan to invade South Vietnam. On December 13 North Vietnam violated the Paris peace treaty by sending troops into Phuoc Long Province in South Vietnam. This was the first step in their invasion of South Vietnam. U.S. President Gerald Ford responded with some diplomatic protests but was adamant he would not resend military ground forces, in compliance with the Congressional ban on all U.S. military activity in Southeast Asia. This was the "greenlight" the North Vietnamese Army had waited for.

Less than a week later, North Vietnam's leaders gathered to formulate their plan for final victory. By the first week in January, the North Vietnamese Army general staff completed their plan for the full invasion of South Vietnam. Their battle plan estimated it would take two years to conquer the South; it took less than six months.

The Vietnam Conflict ended on April 30, 1975, after Communist troops conquered South Vietnam. In two decades of protracted warfare, the Vietnamese people survived the Japanese occupation, endured the French attempt to re-colonizing, and defeated the United States. All the fighting had finally stopped. However, the Vietnamese communists were both jubilant and arrogant toward the rest of Southeast Asia. They considered themselves the new leaders of the region.

The North Vietnamese government in Hanoi decided to change their name from Democratic Republic of Vietnam to Socialist Republic of Vietnam. The name change implied their desire to follow a more socialist model as opposed to communist. The Hanoi government also decided to merge the People's Revolutionary Party of South Vietnam with the Labor Party of North Vietnam, culminating in selecting a new name, Vietnamese Communist Party (VCP). The VCP would be the only legal party in Vietnam. The VCP leader's title was changed from First Secretary, a term used by Chinese Communist, to Secretary General, like the Soviet communists. All these changes were largely cosmetic; the substance of everything remained the same, the party power concentrated at the top, in the Politburo. The revolutionary government then changed the name of Saigon to Ho Chi Minh City, in honor of the now-deceased revolutionary leader.

The new government faced economic issues in their efforts to unify the country. The bombing program conducted by the Americans had taken a severe toll on their farmland, industry, and infrastructure. In the North, twenty-nine of thirty provincial capitals had sustained heavy damage, one-third of them almost destroyed. To attempt to rebuild, they created economic zones. The revolutionary government pronounced their new money exchange; the new rate was five hundred dong for one dong of new currency. Additionally, each family could only bring in a maximum of one hundred thousand dong of old currency. This was a devastating blow to the wealth of South Vietnam.

The Vietnamese Communist Party wanted to neutralize the risks posed by loyalists and other political opponents in the South. If these dissidents remained in society, they might start a counter-revolutionary movement. Therefore, the revolutionary government designed a plan to purge the "old order" by first moving all former military and government officials into "re-education camps." Next, they sent capitalists and Catholic priests to the camps. Everyone was sentenced without trial, the revolutionary government considering itself judge and jury. It is estimated that from one to two and a half million South Vietnamese were sent to these camps. The camps imposed hard labor, brutal discipline, and dire conditions on the prisoners, who all had the despair of not knowing if or when freedom would come. The official number of "campers" who died while incarcerated was estimated at 165,000, but this number is widely considered far too low.

Creating even greater hardships, more than one million of the North Vietnamese population migrated to the south and central regions of the former South Vietnam, displacing more than one million South Vietnamese people, who forcibly relocated them to uninhabited mountainous, forested areas. Many of the former citizens of South Vietnam had become used to their economy being propped up by the United States, and they were ill prepared to develop their economy, especially with the loss of their own wealth. In the South, at least three million civilians were unemployed. Millions scrounged for food. Even the half million prostitutes suffered as they no longer had a customer base.

The next year, on July 2, 1976, Vietnam was officially unified, and the government ordered another money exchange. The new currency was that of the North; the rate of exchange was South Vietnamese four dong for five new dong. With a limitation: Each family could only exchange a maximum of two hundred dong.

Vietnam started provoking surrounding countries in Indochina in early 1977. The provocations started with their neighbor, the Democratic Republic of Kampuchea, formerly known as Cambodia. The leaders of Kampuchea became nervous the Vietnamese would attempt to expand into their territory. Because Vietnam had aligned themselves with the Soviet Union, China looked to build relationships with other countries in the region by providing economic and military assistance to the Khmer Rouge against the Vietnamese.

By April, as Kampuchea and Vietnam opened diplomatic channels, their respective militaries prepared for battle along their common border. Then Red China sent troops into northern Vietnam; they held their position for one month before withdrawing to their original border. Officially, Vietnam attempted to acknowledge their kindred spirits, praising the Vietnamese-Chinese friendship, yet in their schools they taught students about Red China's expansion policy. Plus, the Chinese-Vietnamese were put on watch lists and followed by police.

Throughout the balance of 1977, despite diplomatic dialogue, border skirmishes continued. On December 16, the

Vietnamese retaliated by ordering eight divisions into Kampuchea. As the year came to an end, the Vietnamese army had conquered the bordering territory of Svay Rieng Province, stopping short of entering the provincial capital.

The confrontations between the Vietnamese government and the Kampuchean government continued into the next year. On January 6, the Vietnamese Army had moved within thirty-eight kilometers of Kampuchea's capital, Phnom Penh. However, once Vietnam realized their troops were stretched too thin, without more assistance from the Soviet Union, they withdrew back across the border. This left the beleaguered, vicious Khmer Rouge still in control of the country.

It was those confrontations that pushed the Vuong family to begin to look at escaping their homeland.

With Vietnam engaged in Kampuchea, funds were limited for the very real problems inside Vietnam—namely, the need to feed fifty-eight million people. The solution of the new socialist government was to demand increased production of rice, corn, vegetables and grain crops; as with most socialist programs, this failed to produce the desire results. By 1978, Vietnam, once a net exporter of rice, fell four and a half million tons short of its quota. Additionally, there were also critical shortages of seed, fertilizer, pesticides, farming tools, and machinery. These conditions were worsened by flooding in the late 1970s, and by 1979, civilians in Vietnamese cities were subject to food rationing.

To make matters worse, the United States and its many allies refused to trade with Hanoi, in part because of disputes over missing American servicemen, who they believed were still imprisoned in Vietnam.

In 1978, Vietnam signed a treaty with the Soviet Union, which included the allowance of a naval base in Cam Ranh Bay. Next, the Chinese sent tens of thousands of "advisors" to Cambodia and started training the Cambodian army, which could attack Vietnam from the southwest if China desired.

The running conflict between Vietnam and China boiled over in early 1979. On February 17, 1979, China invaded Vietnam and seized control of several towns. The Chinese advanced twenty-five miles into Vietnamese before encountering stiff resistance. Plus, they had to reinforce the resistance with divisions from Cambodia. Once they had moved their forces to within one hundred miles of Hanoi, the Chinese declared its punitive military operation against Vietnam a success and began to withdraw. Within two weeks they were all back on Chinese territory.

Under poverty, lack of economic freedom, harsh political policies, and the treatment of the new communist government, many South Vietnamese people started to seek ways out of the country. Although a few thousand people had fled Vietnam by boat between 1975 and mid-1978, the exodus began in earnest in September 1978. The vessel *Southern Cross* unloaded 1,200 Vietnamese on an uninhabited island belonging to Indonesia. The government of Indonesia was furious at the people dropped on their shores without formal request. However, they were quickly pacified by the assurances of Western countries that they would resettle the refugees. In October, another ship, the *Hai Hong*, attempted to land 2,500 refugees in Malaysia. The Malaysians declined to allow them to enter their territory and the ship sat offshore until the refugees were processed for resettlement in other countries. Additional ships carrying thousands of refugees soon arrived in Hong Kong and the Philippines; these ships were also denied permission to land.

Many thousands of Vietnamese began to depart Vietnam in small boats, attempting to land surreptitiously on the shores of neighboring countries. To combat this exodus, the revolutionary government changed their strategy and set up roadblocks on the main roads and along the beaches. The Vietnamese people started to leave via smaller boats, bringing the term *boat people* into vogue. They were willing to risk their lives in small, old, and crudely built boats to seek a better life. On the open sea, the boat people encountered deadly storms, starvation, diseases—and pirates. The countries of the region often "pushed back" on the boats when they arrived near their coastline, and boat people cast about at sea for weeks or months looking for a place where they could land. Despite the dangers and the resistance of the receiving countries, the number of boat people continued to grow, reaching a high of 54,000 arrivals in the month of June, 1979, with a total of 350,000 in refugee camps in Southeast Asia and Hong Kong.

The United Nations convened an international conference in Geneva, Switzerland, to resolve the growing illegal immigration of Vietnamese seeking temporary asylum. In the end, the Southeast Asian countries agreed to provide facilities for the refugees, and Vietnam agreed to promote orderly departures. The more developed Western countries agreed to accelerate resettlement. The Orderly Departure Program enabled Vietnamese, if approved, to depart Vietnam for resettlement in another country without having to become a boat person. After long journeys of up to six months, those who were lucky might succeed in reaching refugee camps set up by the United Nations Refugee Agency in neighboring countries.

As a result of the conference, boat people departures from Vietnam declined to a few thousand per month and resettlements increased from 9,000 per month in early 1979 to 25,000 per month. The majority of the Vietnamese went to the United States, France, Australia, and Canada.

The worst of the humanitarian crisis was over, although boat people would continue to leave Vietnam for another decade, often dying at sea or being confined to lengthy stays in refugee camps. An estimated of 200,000-400,000 boat people from the total two million that fled died at sea. Countless horror stories grew up of the miseries, maltreatment, murders, and rapes committed by pirates at sea and the guards inside the camps. This caused many of the formerly free South Vietnamese to give up hope of escape and attempt to assimilate in the unified country.

From the fall of South Vietnam until the mid-1980s, Vietnam lost many of its brightest minds, including the Vuong family. As you will read in *Ring for Freedom*, the Vuong family endured many setbacks on their road to escape from Vietnam. When they finally did get out of the country, they endured hardships and privation, first traveling the ocean, then living in refugee camp after refugee camp. Eventually, though, they made it to the United States. Their hardships were similar in nature to those faced by thousands of previous and subsequent refugees, but the Vuong family was luckier than many. Refugees often faced more extreme conditions. But in the end, the Vuong family has become a strong thread in the rich tapestry of the United States of America. Both the family and their adopted country are stronger for their migration.

Ring of Freedom

Prologue

Steep Price of Freedom

Ho Chi Minh City (formerly Saigon, South Vietnam)

Late March, 1980

The pounding on the front door startled everyone inside the house. Vuong Tu Toan's heart filled with ice. He and his wife, Nha-Y, went to the top of the second-story steps and nervously peered down. *Was it the authorities they had feared the last six months?* he wondered. They had been hiding on Cong Ly Street for a month at the home of Nha-Y's parents, Judge Pham Gia He and his wife, Bao.

Whoever was at the front door continued to pound, pound, pound. As his father-in-law went to the door, the Judge waved them back so they would not be seen. Toan looked at Nha-Y, who was wide eyed with her hand up to her mouth. *Was this a Vietnamese agent or just a constable doing a door-to-door check?* Toan's mind was spinning over all the angles: *Had some of the neighbors informed the officials? There were a lot of residents living in this complex. Have we been betrayed?*

Both nervous fugitives reacted to the Judge's signal and stepped out of view. Toan leaned over and whispered to Nha-Y. "Keep the children quiet."

She hurried back down the hall, while he remained at the top of the steps to listen. *Who's come to the door?*

The Judge turned and boldly opened the door. Toan leaned forward, attempting to peek down the steps, but he could not see. Pham invited the individual in. As he closed the door, he shouted, "Toan, Nha-Y. Một ai đó là ở đây để gặp anh." *Someone is here for you.*

Toan quickly descended the narrow wooden stairway to meet the woman he recognized as Ms. Tam.

Ms. Tam glanced at the older man then back at Toan. "Can we talk privately?"

Toan pointed up the stairs. They ascended single file to the sitting area where they were joined by Nha-Y. Ms. Tam scooted to the edge of the chair, speaking in a low voice. "I have good news, *very good* news. If you're still interested in leaving, I've found somebody who is in the process of organizing an escape to Thailand. Are you interested?"

Nha-Y nudged Toan in the arm to answer her. Her aggressiveness startled him. He frowned at her then looked at Ms. Tam. "Possibly. Do you have any details?"

Nha-Y nervously twirled her hair then flipped it slowly behind her back.

Ms. Tam shook her head no. "Not immediately. We are trying to get a head count. But I would start packing."

Toan drew a deep breath and nodded once. "Get me some details as soon as possible."

Ms. Tam opened her hands palms up toward the married couple and replied, "So you're in. I'll be back as soon as the captain has made his plans known."

As Ms. Tam stepped through the front door, Toan heard his father-in-law scold her. "Next time, don't pound on the door so hard. You scared us."

After Ms. Tam left, Nha-Y returned to take care of the children. Toan sat by himself, thinking. Once it was dark, he went outside and smoked a cigarette. The air was heavy, hot and very humid for this time of year. He slowly scanned the front of his in-laws' home from one end to the other. It was located in one of the nicer neighborhoods in Saigon. It was a very cute three-story home overlooking a large courtyard.

Smoking his cigarette relaxed him. He paused for a moment taking in the view of the majestic trees surrounding the home.

I will likely never see them again, Toan thought, taking a second drag off his cigarette.

Fortunately, the home was large, but with everyone staying there it was overcrowded. *The Judge has done so much to assist us with our escape efforts—gold, money, and now hiding us. He even lent us gold for previous escape attempts.* Toan loved and respected his in-laws so much. He had asked them to go along, but they refused, as they had turned down a previous opportunity right before the country fell. His father-in-law said they were too old to try—besides, the communists would not likely bother him because of his age. Toan's guilt was overwhelming because he and his family had been hiding out there too long. While he had made a little money from clandestinely practicing medicine at the housing complex and gave it to his father-in-law to pay for food in the overcrowded household, he felt inadequate. He stubbed out the cigarette and went back inside to discuss Ms. Tam's latest offer with Nha-Y.

He sat in their small living area and waited for Nha-Y to join him. The longer he sat, the more he thought and the more nervous he became. Toan's family was doing better than ninety percent of the other citizens. *Why should we try to escape? It is a very dangerous proposition. We lost almost everything in previous attempts.*

Nha-Y came in and sat down opposite Toan. Her eyes cut through to his very soul. "We must get out of here." She relaxed for a second and smiled at her loving, caring husband. "I hope Ms. Tam returns soon with some details. I have started to get our things together."

He knew she was all for escaping. He knew her every point by heart. She did not want their son forced to go serve in the battlefields in Kampuchia. He pleaded with her, "We are doing okay here. I am still managing to practice privately. We are making a little bit of money on the side. I have given all of this extra money to your father to support everyone who is hiding out here."

Toan thought he was getting through to her. "We have failed four times. You know these escapes are very dangerous, one part alive, ten parts dead."

Nha-Y sat quietly and looked him directly in the eyes. She leaned forward and grabbed his arm. "It might be ten times more likely that we die, but leave or die doesn't matter. We can't continue to live as we do!"

Tuesday evening, March 25, 1980

Toan thought he heard a light knock on the front door. He went to the top of the stairway and looked down just as the Judge went to the bottom of the stairs and motioned him back. The Judge turned toward the front door. Toan froze in silence, still peeking down.

The Judge cracked the door open, then opened it wide. Ms. Tam and another rugged-looking individual stepped inside. Once again, Toan came down and escorted them upstairs. Ms. Tam introduced the rough-looking individual as Xoi, the boat owner, who was organizing the escape plan. Xoi began to explain in a scratchy voice. He laid out a few details of his plan and said he had room for several more individuals.

"In the morning," he said, "you and your family are to meet some guides. They will lead you to Rach Gia to board my big boat."

Toan twitched his thin mustache as he glanced at his wife, then nodded at Xoi. "Go on."

Xoi squinted his weathered face at Toan as he pursed his lips. "I will, but first, you must agree to my price before I tell you any more. Each adult will cost five taels of gold." He pointed his fingers and nodded toward the pictures of the five children on the side table. "Three taels for each child."

Toan closed his eyes as he tilted his head back. That came to twenty-seven taels of gold, as Quynh Hoa was now an adult. He believed Ms. Tam would get the fifteen taels of gold back from Mr. Phat, so they needed an additional twelve taels. *Maybe. I must bluff.*

Toan hated last-minute plans; he did not get to think them through. It was very frustrating, but he knew he had no choice. He knew his wife's opinion: Act like you have it. He nodded, "I agree."

Xoi gave him a steely eyed stare for a moment.

Toan was concerned about whether he had done right to accept the offer. *Does he know I don't have it? Did my facial expression give it away?*

Xoi leaned back, stroked his facial whiskers and confidently continued to detail his plan. "The guide will break you up into three groups, and each will depart separately for the Luc Tinh bus station. When you arrive there, each group will get another designated guide to lead them to Rach Gia. No one is to bring anything larger than a small bag, the size of a notebook. Anything bigger will be thrown away before leaving." He looked at Nha-Y then Toan. "You *can't* look like you are trying to escape, or that will blow it for everyone." He wagged his finger in front of them. "No refunds on the gold. Once you are committed, there is no turning back. I'm the one taking the risks. Do I make myself clear?"

Toan glanced at Nha-Y. *What have I gotten us into? How will we be able to make it with so few items?* Nha-Y nodded toward the boat owner, so he would pay attention.

Xoi really got their attention with his next comment. "If or when you should meet one another anywhere along the way, each group must pretend to ignore the other groups. Small groups bring less attention." Once again, he gave them each a stare that scared Toan. The boat owner squinted. "Do I make myself clear? That is very important."

The man stopped talking. Toan was so nervous, he knew he had to respond. "Vâng, tôi hiểu." *Yes, I understand.*

With that, Ms. Tam and Xoi got up and left without another word. Toan followed them down the steps. At the front door, Ms. Tam looked back at Toan before she exited. Toan thought she must be looking for some sort of justification. He forced a smile as he stood at the foot of the steps on the main floor. Ms. Tam smiled back, then quickly closed the door.

As soon as the door was closed, Toan went in and sat down with his mother-in-law and began to lay out the plan.

After hearing the entire plan, his mother-in-law demanded that his sister-in-law Hong and Ms. Lien, Hong's very close family friend, be added to the passengers' list. Toan knew he could not debate her, as his in-laws were financing some of their escape attempt. *How am I going to add them to the list?* Toan's frustration climbed even more when he heard that Hong and Ms. Lien only had two taels each, therefore, he would have to come up with six more taels. He closed his eyes and refigured the numbers in his head. *All this gold needed to attempt our escape, some I don't even have and have no assurance of getting.* He drew a deep breath. It was equivalent to over nine thousand U.S. dollars. *An outrageous price for freedom. . . with no guarantee.*

Nha-Y popped into the room and sat down quietly, as they were finishing their conversation. Once everything was decided, she added the perfect conclusion. "I've already packed all of the clothing and the daily-use items we will need. I have packed two items of clothing for each of us. That is all that will fit in the small bags we can take."

Toan cracked a half a smile for just a second. *Like Noah's Ark.*

As everyone started to get up and go their way, Toan commanded, "Everyone sit down for a minute. We are about to embark on this escape attempt, and you must understand we might not make it. Most likely we won't make it, but we are doing this as a family. None of us can swim, none of us know what's on the other side, so the odds are greatly stacked against us. One in a hundred chance of making it. But we are going to do this as a family and if we make it, you all have to make something of your lives. You have to make this effort worthwhile."

Quynh Trang's eyes got great big, and she looked around at her brothers and sisters.

Nha-Y put her arm around Quynh Hoa. "Now, all of the women are going to get together and start sewing the gold rings and currency in the hems of all the clothes. Just in case." Nha-Y got up to go start getting together everything needed to start the sowing project, and her mother followed her.

Toan slowly got up and plodded up the stairs. He went and sat down on the end of his bed. There was one last item he was going to take. Not only did it have real value, but it had personal intrinsic value to him. It was his complete series of Republic of Vietnam stamps. *I have lost about everything else that had any value.* He had collected these stamps for as long as he could remember. His collection included many early Democratic Republic of Vietnam stamps, some of which he had traded for with an Italian journalist when he was a young man.

If I can get them past the constables and get out of here, if needed I could sell them for maybe five thousand US dollars.

As he finished moving around the room, fidgeting and checking items, he looked up at the clock. It was already 3:00 a.m. He had to get some sleep, if only an hour. He pressed his eyes closed as tight as he could. *Will our fifth escape attempt be successful?*

Chapter One

South Vietnam Is Crumbling, Viet Cong in the Midst

Bien Hoa, South Vietnam

Sunday, March 16, 1975

Toan and Nha-Y sat around their large wooden kitchen table after hustling the children off to school. He was admiring her beauty. It was still an hour before he had to report to the hospital for his day shift. He leaned back against the wall, relaxing over a cup of coffee, thinking about lighting a cigarette. Nha-Y looked at him and grasped his free hand. She was deeply concerned about the bad news coming out of the war, but she did not go into any details. As he listened to her passionate statements against the communists, he was unable to give her any comfort with his own words due to his own growing apprehension about the deteriorating conditions. Yet he resisted the temptation to express his true self out of fear of worrying her even more. She brought it up: Should they escape? What kind of life would they be leaving for their five children? It was a concern.

Toan believed they were living the good life. His medical practice and hospital residency provided a very good living for his family. Bien Hoa was a city that had been untouched by the war and not changed much since the Americans had left. His focus was on his private medical practice and his hospital staff position. He had managed to shut out the hard, cold facts for a long time, but it was over the last few days, he'd begun to really pay attention to the developments of the Vietnam war. They were not good.

He looked at her, "Don't worry, honey. Everything is going to be okay." He said it but wasn't very convincing; he could tell she didn't buy it either.

He glanced at the kitchen clock hanging over the sink. As per his usual morning routine, he turned on the small radio on the kitchen table to listen to the VBC and get caught up on the news of the day with his coffee. This morning the reports began with U.S. President Ford's saying again that the U.S. was finished assisting South Vietnam. Toan did not believe it. If South Vietnam was collapsing, Ford would send in some help.

The news got worse: President Thieu issued a statement that he had ordered the military to abandon the two northern districts plus the highland regions of South Vietnam. Thieu's statement included his reason: It was the loss at battle of Ban Me Thuot.

Toan knew the truth was contrary to the President's statement. He'd heard at the hospital, from a staffer who was married to a high-ranking officer in the military, the South Vietnamese soldiers stationed in that town were overrun by the Viet Cong and North Vietnamese soldiers.

Half of the four thousand South Vietnamese troops either surrendered or deserted, including many of the ranking officers, he thought. *It was totally disgusting.* Ban Me Thuot was just two hundred-eighty kilometers to the north of Bien Hoa. The fighting was getting close to home.

The same hospital staffer told him about the North Vietnamese sending troops across the Ben Hai River to occupy the Quang Tri province. The circle was closing.

As the reporter finished the news, Toan reached over and turned it off. He glanced up in time to see Nha-Y's worried look. She floored him with her next comment: "If we should try to escape, it will be complicated by Thanh, since he is only two."

While this had crossed Toan's mind, her comment hit like a slap in the face. He grasped the gravity of her remark, but struggled to ignore it. He looked at his watch—half past eight. He could escape the conversation this time, but he knew Nha-Y well enough. They would revisit the subject eventually. As Toan got up, he stepped around the table to kiss her. "I've to got to get to the hospital."

Nha-Y stood up to meet his lips but didn't let go of her hug until she made one more comment. "I don't want to live under communist rule, Toan. I don't."

As Toan walked through the doorway, Nha-Y exclaimed, "I am going to make up a Pan-Am bag for each of our children, I am going to put in two articles of clothing, some snacks, and their identification with our names in them for each child. Just in case."

Toan continued walking. He knew it was best if he said nothing at this point.

Once at the hospital, Toan—Dr. Vuong, as he was known when he was there—went immediately to the nurse's station before starting his ward rounds. He bid the two nurses good morning as he picked up the clipboard to review patients' charts. As he stood there reading, one of his nurses came up to him. "Did you hear about Ban Me Thuot?"

Toan nodded without looking up and continued to read the charts.

The nurse continued, "My brother's family lived there, they are part of the exodus. Coming out of Pleiku. We have not heard from him in a couple of days. He has a small child in his family. We are so worried." Out of the corner of his eye, he noticed one of other nurses at the station, eavesdropping on their conversation.

That nurse got up from her desk and stepped over to put her arm around the distraught woman. "President Thieu ordered the South Vietnamese military protecting that province and town so that the civilians could evacuate to Saigon." In a consoling voice, she continued, "I'm sure they will be fine."

The first nurse shook her head no. "Many of the troops decided to cut and run. They are now intermingled within the civilians who are trying to escape the North Vietnamese, too."

Toan frowned as he looked at her. "Where did you hear that?"

She picked up a tissue and wiped under her eyes. "My husband is in the military and told me this morning that the whole thing has turned to chaos."

Toan glanced back and forth between the two nurses. These family stories were only adding stress. *Why didn't I arrange for me and my family to leave?*

He had to put their stories out of his mind. He was walking away when he turned the corner to come face to face with Le To Nga, affectionately known as Ms. Nga. She was a pediatric nurse, which was in another area of the hospital. She jerked but still made eye contact with Toan. *Had she been standing there the whole time?*

Ms. Nga stuttered, "I need your assistance down in pediatrics when you can?"

"If it's not urgent, as soon as I have completed my rounds."

Toan was about to leave the hospital for the evening to return to his home office on the first floor. He had scheduled two more appointments before his day was over. Ms. Nga came into his office and closed the door. Immediately, Toan believed there must be a problem with one of the babies. She was a very good nurse and could almost always handle a problem in her work area.

Ms. Nga cleared her throat. "I am being watched by the South Vietnamese police. Will you be there for me when I need you? I won't ask you to help me, but I may need you to help out another way?"

He could not comprehend what she was asking and frowned. "What do you mean? Of course, I'll help out in your area, if needed." He thoughtfully processed what she had said and continued. "But what makes you think the police are watching you? And why?"

Ms. Nga stared at him for a moment. He believed she was parsing her words, carefully choosing what to say next. She spoke softly. "The police have been watching me since the beginning of Tet."

"What have you done, Ms. Nga? I thought you needed help down in Pediatrics."

She shook her head. "It doesn't matter. I need to try to make it to the Bung or some other Viet Cong controlled area right away." Again, she paused for a moment. "I am a Viet Cong secret agent. What I need your help with. . ."

Toan stopped her. "What you want me to help you with won't get me in trouble with the hospital or the law, will it?"

She sat up straight in the chair and stared into his eyes almost defiantly. "I would never ask you to do anything to compromise your good self. I have too much respect for you. I have been managing a fund for the past few months. I want you to take it over, at least temporarily."

Toan started to speak, but Ms. Nga waved her hand back and forth. "My uncle is a high Viet Cong official. Are you going to turn me in?"

Toan was speechless. He tilted his head back and rubbed his chin. He had known people he had suspected but never had anyone come right out and admitted it to him. "Yes, I will take over the fund, temporarily. As to your question about turning you in, you are a good nurse, we need good nurses. If you do not do anything against the staff or the hospital, I will not turn you in. But keep in mind, I will not help you if you get in trouble with the authorities. I can tell you one thing for sure, no matter how high of a rank your uncle has, he will not be able to help you out if you get in trouble. Do I make myself clear?"

She stood up, stepped to the door. As she opened it to leave, she looked back and nodded.

Toan sat for a minute thinking about the strange conversation. He looked at his watch, it was time to go to his private office. All the way to the parking lot and during the drive home, he was fixated on his conversation with Ms. Nga. *Have I done the right thing, saying I won't turn her in?*

Two weeks later, April 1, 1975

Toan was ready to leave the hospital for the day. He had seen so many patients, he was mentally fatigued. He had not had a chance to catch up on any developments for the day. On his way out he decided to go down and check on the surgical area of the hospital. He found Dr. Tran Van Duc, the hospital's chief surgeon, leaning back against the wall in a straight-back chair with his eyes closed. Toan went over and asked. "Are you okay?"

Dr. Duc opened his eyes and looked around to see who had spoken. "Yes, yes. I am fine. Just taking a quick shut-eye between surgeries."

Toan sat down by him.

Dr. Duc asked, "Did you hear about Ms. Nga?"

Toan did not know what to say. The last he had heard she had been arrested, which he acknowledged.

Dr. Duc folded his arms on his chest, as he drew a deep breath. "Well, Dr. Nghiem Xuan Tho, our hospital director and chief of the Bien Hoa Health service, went and bailed her out. She has disappeared."

Toan looked surprised. While he speculated she had gone to the Bung area to hide out, he chose to say nothing and shrugged.

Dr. Duc got up and went to the sink to wash his hands. "You know Dr. Tho is Chinese. Do you suppose he snuck her to China?"

While Toan was aware Tho was Chinese, the thought of him being a communist and bailing out a Viet Cong Agent like Ms. Nga was beyond his imagination. Dr. Duc grabbed a fresh pair of gloves while he continued to stare at Toan but did not say another word.

Toan bid him good evening as he got up from the chair and left the room. He went down the hallway toward the exit, and as he stepped through the glass door to leave the hospital for the evening, the director called out to him from the door to the parking lot. Toan turned around and walked back toward his colleague, who handed him a printout.

Apparently, North Vietnamese forces broke the Laotian cease-fire. Both North Vietnamese and Pathet Lao forces were moving to box in Vang Pao's Hmong defenders. They had blocked the road junction linking Vientiane, Louangphrabang, and the Plain of Jars. The Prime Minister of Royal Laos, Prince Souvanna Phouma, ordered Vang Pao only to defend himself and refused to allow air strikes in his support.

Toan slowly handed the paper back, without a word.

The director waved the paper around. "We need to develop a contingency plan for the hospital. Be thinking about it. I will be calling for a staff meeting in the next few days. We must be prepared for the worst."

Toan pursed his lips, nodded and continued toward the parking lot. On the drive over to his private office, he continued to fret over the events of the last few days. *No good news anywhere. Now, we are going to have a staff meeting to prepare the hospital for exactly what? What is going on with Ms. Nga? Why did she disappear?*

Before he could get to his car he saw one of the nurses from his area sitting on the ground crying. He walked over to her.

"What's the matter?"

She wiped the tears with the back of her hand. "My brother was killed in Pleiku. He was one of the few Marines who remained behind fighting the Viet Cong so the civilians could escape."

Toan had heard on the news that President Thieu had ordered the evacuation of the large city, but he had also learned that the high-ranking officers fled to protect themselves. This turned the evacuation into a total disaster. He looked down at the ground; her story personalized the chaos. He really did not know how to console the poor girl.

"At least he died with honor. Those officers who fled have to live with their conscience."

She sniffled, "They *have* no conscience."

He could hardly argue with her. He turned back to walk to his car. He knew some of the civilians were evacuated by sea with the South Vietnamese Army 1st Corp, but many civilians would be slaughtered like sitting ducks at the hands of the Viet Cong.

As he pulled up to the next stop light, Toan glanced around. He was in the middle of a large number of mopeds with riders on the back, and could hear dozens upon dozens of conversations between the drivers of the mopeds and those riding on the back. The streets were crowded with people walking. First, his eyes were fixated on an old lady with a giant burlap sack on her back as she struggled to peddle her bicycle. Then he noticed a beautiful young lady on a moped with a young man on the back holding an umbrella over her head. When the light turned green, the air was filled with moped horns and accelerating mopeds and automobiles that jumped away from the intersection, while the lam cabs followed behind through the crowded intersection.

As Toan drove down the street, Tin Tin BBQ and Huang Tam were crowded with customers. The whole scene was surreal. *Was it really just another day?* He thought about the way Hue fell without so much as a fight. *After a three-day siege, the South Vietnamese troops again just walked away from the defense of the city.* It was the ancient capital, a symbol of Vietnam for as long as he could remember. *Once again, the citizenry fled the North Vietnamese troops.* A horn sounded behind him. The light had turned green, he stepped on the accelerator and continued toward his home. With each story, Toan became more distressed. Yet despite all these calamities, he could not get the conversation with Ms. Nga out of his head.

As he pulled up in front of his home and walked toward his first-floor private office, there were a few patients standing outside waiting. He forced a smile and nodded for them to follow him in. He helped a little elderly Vietnamese lady into his office. *Perhaps I could find someone to help us escape.*

Before he could see his first patient, Vu came bounding down the steps to help him out in his office.

Chapter Two

The United States Will Not Help

Bien Hoa

Monday, April 21, 1975

Toan walked into his office, turned on the VBC radio station and laid down his stethoscope to wait for his next appointment. It seemed everyone was either listening to the radio or watching television as the conditions around Bien Hoa and Saigon deteriorated rapidly.

Just then, the radio station's regular broadcast was interrupted by a special announcement from President Thieu. Toan leaned over, turned up the radio, and lit a cigarette. From the very beginning, Thieu's voice was broken as he told the country he was resigning as president. He went on to read a letter he had received from U.S. President Richard Nixon, back in 1972, promising severe retaliatory action if North Vietnam threatened South Vietnam. Next, Thieu condemned the Paris Peace Accords, singling out U.S. Secretary of State Henry Kissinger.

"The United States has not respected its promises. It is inhumane. It is untrustworthy. It is irresponsible. The U.S. promised more military aid. In accordance with the peace agreement, the United States was to replace equipment on a one-by-one basis."

Thieu mentioned that the year before the U.S. Congress had cut its funding down to $700 million dollars. He continued, "But the United States did not keep its word. Is America's word reliable these days?"

When Toan heard that he realized it had affected their fight against the North Vietnamese and the Viet Cong.

Lastly, Thieu tried to strike a nerve with the United States: "The United States did not keep its promise to help us fight for freedom, and it was in the same fight that the United States lost 50,000 of its young men."

When Thieu finally finished, Toan looked at his watch. The man had rambled on for almost ninety minutes. When Thieu finished, Toan leaned over and turned off the radio. He believed Thieu's speech would be played in America on the news that evening. That was why Thieu had mentioned the American deaths—to pressure the U.S. government. He placed his elbows on his knees and stared at the wall. He felt like someone had just stomped him into the ground.

Friday, April 25, 1975

Dr. Nguyen Thanh Tung, the chief of Bien Hoa health service, convened a second urgent meeting at the hospital in less than a week. All the highest-ranking residents were required to attend, including doctors, dentists, and pharmacists. The meeting was also open to those employees who wished to attend.

As soon as everyone was seated, Dr. Tung stepped up to the podium, tapped sharply on the microphone which brought a loud, staccato *thump, thump, thump.* Then he shocked all attendees with his first announcement, which was that Dr. Nguyen Thanh Phuoc, director of the hospital, had fled town several days earlier. The police recovered his abandoned Volkswagen, which had been assigned by UNICEF, in Cu Lao. The next announcement was an even bigger surprise to Toan: He had been named the new hospital director. *I don't know whether to be honored, excited, or upset because I was set up to take the fall.*

After the meeting, as Toan was walking out of the conference room, one of the doctors told him that Thieu had been exiled to Taiwan and escorted out of the country by the U.S. Central Intelligence Agency representatives. The doctor leaned over and whispered that Thieu and his key aides had left the country in a plane loaded with suitcases filled with gold. *How does he know this?* Toan shrugged his shoulders. *It's probably true.*

On the drive home from the hospital that evening, Toan was chastising himself. He'd still failed to do anything for his family's sake, and now he feared he was too late. This evening he did not take the direct route home—driving helped him think. Unfortunately, he could not drive out into the countryside because, according to the radio and television reports, the North Vietnamese army was closing in on the area. Since the day two years earlier when Thanh had been born, their lives had not been affected despite the ongoing conflict. Nha-Y still taught Vietnamese Literature at Ngo Quyen High School, and he had hired several maids to help her around the house, so she could focus on the five children. The Vuong family was living well, but that seemed about to change.

Toan parked his Opel and walked into their home. Nha-Y did not greet him at the door as usual, and the voices of children came from various places around the house. He guessed he would find Nha-Y somewhere near Thanh. When he found her, he walked over and kissed her. He asked his wife to pack up some clothing and various sundries for the family. That night he wanted to take his family to her parents' home in Saigon. When she protested, he told her that there was a rumor in the next few days the North Vietnamese and Viet Cong troops could occupy Long Thanh on their way to Bien Hoa and the airbase.

This motivated Nha-Y to pack; it was only then that Toan mentioned his promotion. "It is like being told to pilot a sinking ship."

As soon as it was dark, Nha-Y and the five children were all loaded into their Opel sedan. Toan looked around and forced a smile to all of his family then drove off onto the back roads toward her parent's home. Toan had heard that many South Vietnamese forces were stationed outside of Bien Hoa, holding off the advancing enemy. He considered the back roads his best chance to get his family to safety. As they turned onto one of the streets that were normally lined with patrons, all the small markets and shops were closed up tight. The vehicle traffic was heavy for this time of the evening, but there was very little foot traffic. The residents may have already battened down, preparing for the looming enemy. As he pulled up in front of his Pham residence, Toan was satisfied his choice of back streets made their twenty-kilometer trip uneventful.

The next morning, Nha-Y, Toan, and his brothers and sisters-in-law were crowded around the radio and the television seeking any news they could gather. Saigon was in severe turmoil. Much of the discussion on the radio focused on President Nguyen Van Thieu's exile and his handing over of his powers to Vice President Tran Van Huong. Toan thought his situation at the hospital was bad until he heard this news. *Talk about being handed a sinking ship.* The radio station they were listening to detailed all of President Thieu's actions and focused on the fact that he had abandoned his people and protected only himself and his immediate staff by driving off in his Mercedes Benz limousine with all his tons of gold, jewels, and other valuable articles. *Apparently, my doctor friend had good sources.* Still, Toan was distraught after listening to the news.

On Monday morning, Toan decided he had to report to the hospital. That had been the consensus of the physicians on Friday. Show unity. If they could not get to the hospital, they were to meet at the Health Ministry, which was in a more secure, central location. He sat in his Opel, stared out the front window for several minutes before starting the car. *Off to my first official day as the hospital director. What exactly does a hospital director do on a day that the Viet Cong or the North Vietnamese Army could be on our very doorstep?* He pushed the key in the ignition and turned it.

He had no idea what he would find on the road. The day before it had been reported that the city was encircled by the North Vietnamese Army. Supposedly, it was now being defended by 30,000 of South Vietnam's best and bravest soldiers, but Toan knew two things no one was saying: First, they were virtually leaderless due to desertion rate at the highest command, and second, so what? Saigon was being "defended." Were the North Vietnamese going to let Saigon stand alone, like Singapore? Of course not. All they could do is prolong the agony or, god forbid, siege the city. Toan knew one thing: He did not want to eat rats to survive.

On the twenty-kilometer drive to Bien Hoa, he buzzed through the traffic. No one was traveling in the same direction as him. *They must be running from the Viet Cong.* Several kilometers away from Bien Hoa and before the bridge into the city, he turned the corner and saw a South Vietnamese military roadblock several streets ahead. He ran his hand over the top of his head. *Got to avoid the military, can't get to the hospital.*

Toan spun his car around and took off as fast as he could go, but now he was in heavy traffic, including commercial buses with their fumes. Time for the back-up plan. Since he couldn't get to the hospital, all the doctors had agreed to rendezvous at the office of Health Ministry.

By the time he arrived, he was met by most of the hospital staff, Vu Nguyen Bich and Trinh Dinh Tri, plus several doctors from other provinces. After a few minutes of brief conversations, all of them were hustled into an emergency meeting with director-general Dr. Truong Minh Cac and bureau chief of Health, Nguyen Chi Nhieu. They reviewed current developments.

Afterwards, Dr. Cac ordered all of them to register then go home: "Be with your families. Everyone should attempt to make it to the health ministry every day, if possible, you know, to show unity and resolve."

As Toan started toward the door leading to the hallway, Bich pulled him and Tri aside. "I really believe the situation here is bleak."

Toan and Tri exchanged glances. *Was he expecting either of us to argue with him?*

Then came the clincher: Bich whispered, "I am going to attempt to flee the country."

All the way back to his in-laws, Bich's words played over and over. *Did Bich have a plan or was he just putting something together? Had Toan put his family at risk by not escaping? Or would he be putting them a greater risk if they tried?* He knew where Nha-Y stood. And he had plenty of time to replay everything over and over in his head as the street traffic was stop and go. Mostly stop.

By the time Toan finally made it back to his in-laws' home, everything seemed normal in their nice Saigon neighborhood. *Should I be relieved? Which is real? How are the NVA and Viet Cong going to take Saigon?* Over a quick lunch with Nha-Y, Toan described what he had seen, how he could not make it to the hospital. *In reality, it didn't seem any different than when the VC attacked Saigon during Tet 1968.* Deep down, he knew it was different even though it sounded the same. *Why? The Americans weren't here like Tet 1968.* As he finished eating and was sipping on his coffee. "Let's take a drive around town and see what is going on. Get the kids."

Within minutes, Nha-Y and the five children piled into their Opel sedan and off they went for a drive around Saigon. It was a sunny day. Under normal circumstances it would be a fun day to take a drive. He drove toward the business district. But typical of Saigon afternoons, it got hot and muggy fast, even with the windows down. Part of the problem was the stop-and-go heavy traffic throughout the city. To make matters worse, there were no policemen managing traffic. He shook his head. "The entire countryside population who could make it to Saigon are obviously here. This city isn't set up to handle this dreadful situation."

Nha-Y just continued to stare out the window. The view was sad but strangely captivating. Along the streets and sidewalks, helmets, boots, backpacks, medals, insignia, and military equipment of every sort were thrown all around. All public offices and private markets were closed; they had been broken into anyway, damaged and looted. *Civilians are looting.* Toan shook his head in an exaggerated fashion as he witnessed things he had never imagined in his wildest dreams. The picturesque city of Saigon was disappearing before his eyes.

Nha-Y nervously suggested that they try to find out if others were evacuating besides Dr. Bich. Toan wheeled the car around and drove off toward Tan Son Nhut Airbase, but street traffic was blocked by the military. He found the same situation when he attempted to get to Chuong Duong wharf. The military had the roads blocked. In the heart of the city, they witnessed several intersections crammed with buses overloaded with people, their worldly possessions loaded on top.

He quickly turned around again to get away from this dangerous situation and drove off toward the offices of foreign countries: blocked. Lastly, they tried to get down to embassy row to see if they could get to the U.S. Embassy on Thong Nhat Boulevard. *No chance.* All these places were completely locked down either by the constabulary, the military police, the Vietnamese military, or the US Marines. He understood the South Vietnamese soldiers who remained in uniform and tried to follow their orders would be killed or imprisoned, but it was still hard to accept.

They drove past Saigon's Notre Dame Basilica. It was a reminder of times past, a symbol of the French presence in the country several decades earlier. The site caused him to flash back to Hanoi, December 19, 1946, when he was a child and his father was leading them out of town to get out of the crossfire between the French troops and the self-defense militants. But today's situation was ten times more intense.

He realized it had been a mistake to bring his family out in this, particularly, Nha-Y. Most of his children could in no way grasp what they were witnessing, but he saw Nha-Y's fear and frustration. He had only made her more worried.

On the drive back toward his in-laws' home, Toan felt as though they were suffocating inside the car. Clearly, his attempt to dispell stress only compounded matters. He looked down at the temperature gauge and saw the car was overheating. He swung it to the curb and shut off the engine. This only made the situation more tense; they were parked in the middle of chaos. To complicate matters, Nha-Y complained about the predicament they were in and some of the children were crying. Toan felt helpless, at the total mercy of the car. All he could hope was that no one would bother him and his family.

They sat in the car for a couple of hours, until evening was setting in. To his surprise, despite the almost constant stream of desperate people flooding by them as they sat smoldering in the heat, they were not harassed. The car had cooled sufficiently and he restarted it. He drove as rapidly as possible for his in-laws' home. He certainly did not want to be out at night with his family.

Chapter Three

Siege of Saigon

Saigon

Tuesday, April 29, 1975

Toan and Nha-Y had been awakened in the early morning; Thanh had had a bad night. In the still of the morning in the quiet house, they could hear rocket fire in the distance. He was already on his third cup of coffee and cigarette and was anxious to find out what was going on around the city. At six oclock in the morning, Toan flipped on the radio to hear VBC radio beginning its morning broadcast. What were the Viet Cong and North Vietnamese armies up to?

Toan got his early morning news on the worsening disaster that was unfurling in Saigon and South Vietnam. After a quick breakfast, listening to the radio for about an hour, he turned off the radio and made a beeline for his car. He wanted to assess for himself the ever-deteriorating situation in Saigon. He turned on his car's radio to keep up with the current developments.

At first, the traffic on the streets was much lighter than the day before, only a few vehicles on the road, the spectacle less disordered, more deserted than the previous day. Toan arrived at the Ministry of Health in less than half an hour. As he pulled up to the front gate, he glanced at his watch: 9:00 a.m. The main gate was hermetically closed, nobody around. Everyone must have been dismissed. *Why wasn't I informed?* He huffed out his breath.

Toan decided to drive over to his sister's family home. He wanted to see if she was interested in leaving the country. He drove past an American office that had been looted, files and papers thrown all over the streets. This increased his anxiety. Then the song "White Christmas" came on the radio. *How strange! In April? What's the matter with the disc jockey?*

Every time he believed conditions could not get worse they seemed to magnify. Continuing on, he saw more looters in the streets with tables, chairs, refrigerators, air conditioners, books, and boxes. This was not the way of the Vietnamese people he knew, yet it was exactly what he was witnessing.

He parked in front of Minh's home, burst in the front door and shouted, "Do you want to try to escape the communists?"

Minh was sitting there calmly listening to the VBC. She placed her hands on her lap as she looked at him and simultaneously slurped her tea. "I have no interest in leaving my country. Besides, at this point it would be useless to try." Then she began to babel some useless story. "I heard nephews Anh and Ai are talking about some neighbor having gotten to carry home a box containing antibiotics."

Dejected and distraught at her attitude, he left. He drove off to look for his brothers Huong, Trong, and Cat. One by one, he picked them up and all four of them were in the car when the disc jockey interrupted the news with a special announcement: "The South Vietnamese National Assembly has received the resignation of President Huong and appointed General Duong Van Minh."

Big Minh is the president, yet again, Toan thought. What expectations could they possibly put on him?

The special announcement on the radio continued: "President Minh appointed Vu Van Mau as his prime minister. Minh offered a cease-fire to the North Vietnamese leaders. He has offered to form a combination and reconciliation government with the Viet Cong and the Democratic Republic of Vietnam. As of this time there is no response from their leaders."

The four of them rode silently all the way back to Toan's in-laws' residence where they sat on the terrace and watched intently the steady stream of helicopters flying in and out of Tan Son Nhut. Later, it appeared that helicopters were coming in and out from the area where the U.S. Embassy was located. Periodically, Toan glanced at his brothers. He could tell they were all as frustrated as he was watching Americans and U.S. Embassy staff being removed from the fray.

The shelling from the North Vietnamese seemed to get more intense as the day went on. Toan figured that was the North Vietnamese answer to President Minh's coalition proposal—a pounding *no.*

Now, their focus was not only the helicopters in the air but traffic on the street below. A steady stream of the people of Saigon drove, walked, and ran toward the center of town. As the afternoon turned to evening, the sound of the helicopters became more ominous. Their constant thump, thump, thump beat into Toan's head his family's fate—within days, maybe even hours, they would be stuck in Vietnam under the rule of the communists.

Maybe an hour before dark, they witnessed a Vietnamese helicopter circling some houses nearby for what seemed like a half hour, then at last it flew away. Toan commented to his brothers the pilot must have been ordered to pick up some high-ranking official or high-ranking officer, who must have already left.

That evening, Toan's immediate family and Nha-Y's family crowded around the kitchen table. They were stacked two and three deep. The kitchen was full and the atmosphere very tense. Toan already knew Nha-Y's feelings; she was one hundred percent against the communists. However, Toan was more confused and unsure of what his next move should be. His youngest child was just two. As Nha-Y had pointed out in the past, escaping with someone that young would be a task. Quynh Trang was four; she would be a handful also. The radio was blaring up-to-date information, and none of it was good. The Americans and key personnel were being sent to three U.S. aircraft carriers sitting off-shore.

Perplexed, Toan looked around the table and listened to everyone's comments. Strange—nobody talked about leaving or staying. Nha-Y's father was first to get up, bidding everyone good night as he quietly walked over to the stairway and went upstairs. After he left, over the next few minutes the conversations fell silent. Those who remained at the table took turns pushing away from it and slowly shuffling to bed. Exhausted, Toan was the last one seated. He remained by himself, thinking, replaying what he had witnessed during the day and over the last week. Distraught by his failure to get his family out of South Vietnam, he listlessly went upstairs to lie down on brother Huong's bed in the small room on the second floor. However, he was unable to reach sound sleep, tossing and turning on the bed. Rest seemed impossible. Several times, he got up to smoke a cigarette. His frustration continued to rise as it had ever since leaving their home in Bien Hoa a few days earlier. At some point in the wee hours of the morning, he finally fell off to sleep.

He had not been asleep long when he was startled awake by the loud backfire of a truck and yelling and shouting from the street below. Toan leaped up and was at the window in two strides. He witnessed some dozen people fighting to climb up into an old truck. His eyes zoomed in on his brother Huong struggling to get in, a backpack in one hand, the other attempting to grab hold of the side of the truck. Toan let out the breath he had been holding. *I hope he is able to escape.*

Back in bed, Toan put his arm across his forehead. Immediately, his mind raced back to the events that had transpired over the previous weeks, despite his efforts to shut them off. *I can't shut these thoughts down, I need sleep.*

After drifting off to sleep, Toan was startled awake again by a loud pop that jolted him out of bed. Again, there were loud voices outside. He had no idea if he had just fallen asleep or had slept for a while, but he ran to the window and looked outside. It was still dark. He came to his senses and realized it was a car backfiring on the street below. There must have been at least a dozen people in front of the house. He turned and started running down the steps toward the living room. He sprinted to the front window and leaned out over the couch. Then he saw Huong slowly walking up the sidewalk, carrying his backpack. The man looked like hell, his clothes disheveled and untidy, like he'd been in a fight. Huong pounded on the front door.

Once seated in the living room, a distraught Huong began to relay his story. The truck he had hopped in had driven around all night, attempting to get to anyplace to escape: Tan

Son Nhut airport, Chuong Duong Wharf, the U.S. Embassy, anywhere and everywhere they could think of. At one place after another they encountered numerous constables or military policemen, even troops of different branches of service stopping people, declaring those sites off limits. Huong lowered his head. No one was permitted to reach an airplane or a ship in order to get out of Saigon.

Toan did his best to comfort his brother, but there was little he could say or do.

Chapter Four

U.S. Embassy Evacuation,
South Vietnam Abandoned

Saigon

Wednesday, April 30, 1975

Toan was up early in the morning, once again with little sleep. After smoking a cigarette on the terrace, he decided to check the morning news. What had transpired the night before? When he got to the living room, his father-in-law was already there quietly listening to the radio. *A military judge, then a Saigon district judge,* Toan thought. *I wonder what he is thinking. How will his life be affected by the Communist takeover? I hope they don't lock him up.* When the reporting turned to what had happened—and was still happening—at the U.S. Embassy, the Judge turned off the radio and switched on the television, hoping to see the developments.

The Judge found a local station with a reporter and a camera man reporting what seemed like thousands of South Vietnamese attempting to break through or climb over the fence to get into the compound. Unfortunately, they were met by plenty of U.S. Marines in full combat gear. Both Toan and his father-in-law were captivated by the desperation playing out.

Soon, others in the household joined them in front of the television. Over the next couple of hours, they watched the situation descend into pure chaos as the South Vietnamese civilians continued their attempt to get into the compound, climbing the tall fence only to be forced back.

Suddenly, the news feed abruptly stopped. They turned off the television and turned the radio back on. They picked up the middle of radio news feeds discussing other developments, which were just as damning. The National Liberation Front troops were quickly invading and occupying the central region of South Vietnam. Now they were fighting to take Xuan Loc, the province seat of Long Khanh, just thirty kilometers from Bien Hoa. South Vietnamese airplanes had dropped cluster bombs that had been left by the U.S. Air Force. The Viet Cong sustained huge losses, but they were relentless and kept coming. One story reported that despite the roadblocks around

Tan Son Nhut, a significant number of South Vietnamese civilians made it there and swarmed the helicopters, to no avail. Toan marveled at that as he had witnessed the security surrounding the base.

Toan decided to go outside and was joined by several other family members. They watched the constant stream of helicopters landing and taking off from the U.S. Embassy heliport on top of its highest building. At first it was mesmerizing, but after a few minutes it became depressing. Toan went back inside and turned the television back on. At 8:35 a.m., the local television station brought back their feed outside the U.S. Embassy and announced that the last Americans, ten Marines, had lifted off from the roof top and left Saigon, concluding the United States presence in Vietnam. *I never thought I would see this day.*

Once again, the television news feed dropped. Toan took a visual inventory of everyone's faces in the room: They were all gloomy. He believed everyone knew what was next. The North Vietnamese troops would pour into Saigon at any minute with little or no resistance.

Toan's brother Huong turned on the radio and cranked up the volume. No one moved. Everyone remained silent, listening to the radio broadcast. Then the feed was interrupted by an announcement that the new President Minh was about to speak. Toan turned around and looked at the clock; it was 9:00 a.m. Minh gave the order to the military of all ranks to lay down their arms to avoid confrontation. He asked the revolutionary troops to secure public offices, to excuse civilians. The last thing he said brought the room to their figurative knees: "We are waiting to welcome you."

Toan grasped for words to utter but nothing came out; the Republic of South Vietnam had unconditionally surrendered and was ready to hand power to the National Liberation Front and the North Vietnamese. Minh had accepted unconditional surrender terms from the North Vietnamese.

I will remember this day for the rest of my life as National Regret Day, Toan thought. *For the populace and for the military of the Republic of Vietnam.* He went outside to smoke a cigarette. *The country, my country of South Vietnam doesn't exist anymore. It only lasted a little more than twenty years. Gone from the map, just like that.*

As he stood outside taking it all in and thinking about what had just happened, he wiped a tear from the corner of his eye. *There was no longer a South Vietnam. I cannot believe the North Vietnamese army defeated the South with such lightning speed.* As Toan snubbed out his cigarette and turned to walk back into the house, he looked the nice home up and down. *What will happen to Nha-Y's father? Will the North Vietnamese round up all military and government officials? If so, then what?*

Following the announcement by President Minh, many residents of the complex came outside to talk and share their thoughts. They were quite gloomy. The common theme was when they would see the revolutionary troops, the dreaded Viet Cong and the North Vietnamese Army, marching into the city. The residents were all quite anxious. As the hour approached 11:00 a.m., they could hear the distant rumble of tank tracks on the concrete streets coming in their direction.

Most of those gathered on the lawn slowly moved toward Cong Ly Street. A few went back into their homes. Within a couple of minutes, Toan was joined on the curb by Quynh Hoa, Vu, and Quynh Dao. Quynh Dao looked up at her father and asked, "What is making that noise, Father?"

Toan looked each of his children in the eyes and replied, "It is either the North Vietnamese Army or Viet Cong Army tanks coming our way."

Vu heard the clacking coming down the street. It was a unique sound but his father's explanation made sense—metal tracks on concrete. Vu did not know any children his own age at his grandfather's home, so he remained standing with his father. He pushed his way to the curb in front of everyone.

Quynh Dao continued to maintain eye contact with her father. "Are they going to hurt us? Mother says she doesn't like them."

"No, they are just going to Presidential Palace."

As the clanking of the metal cleats got louder and louder, residents from both sides of Cong Ly Street appeared carrying bamboo-handled blue-and-red flags with the yellow star, the Viet Cong flag. Toan looked around in total disbelief. At the head of the street, the first tank appeared, rolling down the middle of the street. There were two soldiers, one stationed at the machine gun, which was pointed in the air, while the other was in the open turret. Each of them wore helmets with stars in the middle. As they rode by, they scowled at the people lining the street, despite everyone waving their flags and cheering—cheering the conquerors. Right behind them was another tank, then an armored vehicle with three soldiers riding on top. This was followed by three more tanks, then came a World War II jeep with five soldiers in it. None of them had helmets on. One of them in "black pajamas"—supposedly some of the most vicious fighters—stood on the jeep with a Viet Cong flag. All of them were holding AK-47s straight up in the air except for the driver. *Never in my wildest dreams did I expect to witness such a spectacle.*

Quynh Dao looked in the direction of the tanks; simultaneously, she threw her hands up to her ears. Quynh Dao glanced around to see what Quynh Hoa was doing; the sound did not seem to be affecting her. She was just looking around at the crowd on the street. Everybody on the street seemed to have Viet Cong flags except for Quynh Dao's family. They were all waving them wildly and seemed to be having fun. *Were these people communist sympathizers or were they just out here acting?* she wondered.

Vu thought, *I would love to ride through town standing up in a jeep. My father would never let me do it, but it sure looks like fun. But these were Viet Cong, the enemy of my country.* His excitement waned immediately. He looked back at his father, whose face reminded Vu this was the Enemy. These were the people he had heard his mother and father talk about. He was ready to go back inside even though the military parade wasn't over.

As the tank parade passed in front of them, the sound was almost deafening. Toan looked around at his children. Quynh Hoa was just staring straight ahead, Vu was glancing back and forth between his father and the street, while Quynh Dao had her hands over her ears. It suffocating and insulting in the deepest parts of Toan's soul. It was worse than Toan remembered from when he was a young boy, when the French occupied Ninh Binh while he was attending school in Phuc Nhac back in 1944.

Toan looked at Vu and Quynh Hoa. "You children go back inside."

They nodded as Quynh Hoa pulled Quynh Dao's hands from her ears to start to tug her inside. The sight of watching his children walk back toward the home was strangely unnerving to Toan.

He decided to follow the parade as the last tank passed. The disgusting parade of Viet Cong armor lasted for fifteen minutes. He had to see for himself the fall of the presidential palace. The Viet Cong did not bother to open the gate; they just drove straight through it. The two wrought-iron gates went flying five or six feet before getting crushed under the line of tanks and armored vehicles.

Toan stopped at that spectacle, soaking it into his mind. It was a devastating vision. Within another twenty minutes, a very large red-and-blue Viet Cong flag was raised over the presidential place. Toan looked down at his watch; it was a few minutes before 11:00 a.m. It was like a dagger in his heart. He and his family were now under communist rule.

He turned slowly and walked back up the street; the revelers lining the street also returned to their homes. There was no more cheering, only the cleat marks left in the concrete as a reminder of the parade. The street had returned to the way it had been in the morning before the surrender.

When he entered the Pham residence, Toan was greeted by long, quiet faces. The Judge got up from his favorite chair and barked. "You missed President Minh's message of unconditional surrender, claiming the war was over."

Toan did not say a word. While he had not heard the speech, he did not need to. He had witnessed it moments before at the presidential palace. *I'll never forget the scene I just witnessed.* He looked around the room at those sitting with blank looks on their faces.

He went upstairs to be with Nha-Y and his children. At the moment, it was the only thing that had meaning to him—his family.

When evening came, all the members of both families crowded around the dinner table in the kitchen. However, hardly any of them, except for the children, could eat. They all just pieced over the plates. Nha-Y, who had not touched her plate at all, pushed away from the table, went over and turned on the radio again. Everyone knew the new revolutionary government was in control of all communications, but she emphatically stated that they must know what was going on and what was to be expected, since they were all stuck here in the "new" Vietnam. There was a message being repeated over and over. It was from the city Military Executive Commission asking the populace to stay calm as the Liberation Forces had prevailed in all provinces in South Vietnam. With that comment, Toan's brother Huong jumped up and snarled, "That's just not true."

His comment cracked through the silence, and everyone looked at Huong.

He continued, "Not all provinces in the west region of South Vietnam have been taken over. I spoke to several people today as I traveled around the city."

The revolutionary government radio broadcast continued, "Tomorrow, May first, will be celebrated as Labor Day. All of Saigon's residents shall gather in the square at Thong Nhat Avenue in front of the former Independence Palace. Until then, all citizens of Saigon are ordered to stay in their homes unless they have an emergency. To prevent the break-in and looting of facilities and stores, violators will be severely punished."

As the radio broadcast continued, Toan glanced at Nha-Y then at his children then back at his wife, "Since I am in charge of the Bien Hoa Hospital, in the morning I must go to that town meeting and make preparations to return to start running the hospital until I receive further orders."

When Toan went to bed that night all he could think about was that the day would be forever branded in his brain as National Regret Day.

Chapter Five

Labor Day: Dawn of a New Day

Saigon

Saturday, May 1, 1975

Despite the new revolutionary government's orders for all residents to attend the Labor Day meeting, Toan decided to sleep in. He had not slept well for days. When he finally arose, Nha-Y prepared a small breakfast for him. Over his last cup of coffee, she inquired if he had reservations about missing the Labor Day meeting. Toan acted like he was not concerned, but the truth of the matter was that he was. Toan talked Nha-Y into joining him for a quick trip over to his sister Minh's home, just to make sure she was okay.

The traffic on the streets was very light, mostly mopeds, almost no cars. After a short visit with Minh, he determined she was okay and mostly unaffected by the fall of the South

Vietnamese government. They decided to drive by the Labor Day meeting. They got there just before it ended. When the crowd was dismissed, Toan and Nha-Y decided to cruise around Saigon.

Despite the hour, there was still very little traffic on the city streets, even fewer walkers. That was very unusual. The remnant of the past few days remained, papers still blowing up and down the streets, military clothing and equipment scattered everywhere. *Those soldiers who ditched their belongings believe that will keep them out of concentration camps,* Toan thought. *They are delusional.*

Before going back to his in-laws' residence, Toan worked up enough nerve to drive by the Independence Palace. During the drive, Nha-Y said to Toan, "You should talk to Father about us returning home."

Toan nodded without a word.

Nha-Y continued, "We need to get back. We need to return to whatever semblance of life we have."

Toan understood. She needed to get back to her home, the place she felt safe. But he knew she was torn, worrying about the fate of her father now that the Viet Cong were in charge. Both of them had been in reflective moods since returning from the main gate of the Presidential Palace—still in wreckage from being run over by tanks—where the National Liberation Front flag was flying high. The reality continued to be heartbreaking.

When they returned to Nha-Y's parents, there was again a gathering of housing complex residents outside visiting with one another. Toan and Nha-Y walked up and joined their conversations, which revolved around everyone's anxiety and embarrassment. Toan was a little more reserved this evening after witnessing so many neighbors out waving the Viet Cong flags. *How many were actually communist sympathizers?* Their discussions only depressed Toan and Nha-Y more, and they went inside for dinner.

The dinner table talk was the fate of their immediate family. Everyone agreed that of all the family members, Thu had the best situation as he was abroad in college. They had received word Thuy's family had been able to escape, but no one had heard from them. The most troubling situation was that no one had heard from Chinh's family. As they finished talking about the family, the Judge turned on the radio to get the latest news coming out of the area. The radio broadcast noted that the roads leading outside of Saigon were now re-opened.

It got quiet around the table. Toan glanced at Nha-Y, who nodded at him then toward her father. Toan got the hint. He looked at the Judge, "Is it okay with you if we return to Bien Hoa in the morning?"

Early the next morning, Toan and his family piled into the Opel, bid their in-laws goodbye, and went on their journey home to Bien Hoa. They experienced their first direct impact of the communist takeover when on the way they stopped for gas—and paid five times the previous rate per liter. Toan glanced around as much as he could while driving, his eyes darting between the road and everything else along each side. The streets of Saigon were barren, still strewn with papers and military clothing. As they got to the outskirts of Saigon, there was destruction everywhere from the Viet Cong shelling. Two days had passed since the takeover, yet weapons were lying along the road. They even saw a destroyed tank, just sitting there. The scene was surreal. As they approached their hometown, nothing was open. There was total silence in the car, the children as wided-eyed as their parents. Toan leaned over to Nha-Y and whispered, "I'm going to drive by some of our favorite restaurants."

From the look on Nha-Y's face, Toan could tell she wasn't the least bit interested the venture. Needless to say, nothing was open. However, there was little damage around Bien Hoa.

It appeared the South Vietnamese Army had surrendered and abandoned Bien Hoa, letting the enemy, the Viet Cong, just walk in. *So sad.* Toan drove past City Hall: There a Viet Cong flag flew high. Before going to their home, he wanted to go by the hospital. Nha-Y was impatient to get home and the children were getting very restless, but he decided to go anyway. As he approached the façade of Bien Hoa hospital, there was a steady stream of people going inside, while others stood or sat outside. Why was that? Toan frowned and turned toward Nha-Y.

"I've got to report to the hospital tomorrow." His attention was drawn back to the people standing and sitting outside. "This afternoon let's get everything organized in our home first."

With great anticipation, Toan pulled the Opel in front of the house; everyone threw the doors open and bounded out of the car. Toan raised his voice. "Hold on, hold on. Let me go through the house and make sure it is safe to enter. Everyone needs to wait out here."

On his command, the family stopped in the middle of the yard and looked at him. Quynh Hoa had to run and pick up Quynh Trang to keep her from running into the house. He checked the front door: It was still locked. He unlocked it and went through every room, even checking the closets. When he was satisfied, he returned to the front door and waved everyone in. They almost knocked him down stampeding through the front door. As he walked to the car, he realized it was up to him to carry in all their belongings. Every time he carried a load into the house, he seemed to bump into one of his children coming out of their bedroom or doing something around the house. He smiled—it was the first time he could remember having something to be happy about for several days. With the unpacking finished, his frustration and stress turned to the contentment of being home. The one place he could find some solitude.

They had not been home for very long when there was a knock at the front door. Nha-Y shouted, "Toan, can you get the door? See who it might be?"

Several more times, the knocking.

Quickly, Toan put on a fresh change of clothes then skipped down the steps. When he opened the door, he was surprised to see Ms. Nga, the nurse and Viet Cong agent, and another lady, who looked to be about fifty years old. Ms. Nga sternly looked at him as she introduced the other lady. "This is my comrade, Dr. Nguyen ThI Thanh. May we come in?"

Toan wasn't sure quite what to expect. He stepped aside and motioned for them to go upstairs. They followed him upstairs and sat down in their living room. Ms. Nga looked at Dr. Thanh then to Toan and spoke in an exaggerated loud voice. "The revolutionaries have officially assumed control of the Bien Hoa hospital." She pointed at Dr. Thanh. "Sister Hai Thanh has been assigned to the facility as the hospital director."

Toan nodded. He didn't say a single word and didn't know what to expect from Ms. Nga. She smiled at him as she received a nod from Sister Hai Thanh. This time her voice returned to normal. "We are pleased that you and your family have returned to Bien Hoa. We assume you intend to resume your work at the hospital."

Toan thought it was almost a command. Obviously, it was best to continue to hear them out and discuss anything regarding his return to Bien Hoa.

Ms. Nga paused as she looked at him, and then continued. "Dr. Tran Van Duc stayed and has been operating on civilians and soldiers from both sides day and night over the last several days." She paused again then looked back at Sister Hai Thanh. "We would like to see the hospital return to the same level of service as before and want you to be a part of it. We consider you an asset. When you report to work, we will see where we think your talents will be best applied."

Toan glanced at both women. He felt compelled to accept whatever role they put him into. He needed the work for his family. "I'll be in in a few days. I'll go wherever you need me." He nodded in an affirming way. "Thank you."

They both seemed pleased with his answer. Ms. Nga let out a deep breath. "We will leave you and your family now."

Toan walked them to the front door and showed them out. He had wanted to ask Ms. Nga what had happened to her since he had last seen her, but it hadn't seemed like the right time.

Exhausted from the day's events and considering he had spent little time with his family, Toan went and found Nha-Y to discuss his conversation with Ms. Nga. After she agreed with his decision, Toan took a bath and went to bed.

Early Saturday morning, Toan decided to walk to the Bien Hoa hospital. The streets were empty of traffic. As was expected, all the stores were closed, but to his surprise many of the private homes appeared unoccupied. *Surely, it was not possible for all of them to escape.* He did find a couple of street vendors along the way to pick up a bowl of rice and a cup of coffee with milk.

Upon arriving at the hospital Toan entered his former office, finding the new hospital director, Sister Hai Thanh, and Ms. Nga, sitting there. Ms. Nga said, "We all have new assignments, Doctor. I have been assigned to the position of the head of medical affairs."

Ms. Nga had barely finished her statement when Sister Hai Thanh spoke up without mincing words. "Dr. Vuong, we are assigning you to the outpatient department to classify patients."

Toan took her look to be dismissive, so he took the hint and left the office without another word. He walked toward Outpatient. *Wonder who else has been assigned to new areas?*

At his new station, there were already many people who had been wounded in the Viet Cong attacks. Quickly, he jumped into action, sending the slightly injured to Mr. Hieu, a minor surgery nurse, while he sent the more severely injured to Dr. Tran Van Duc in the operating room. Once he caught up with everyone in the waiting area, he made the rounds to the medical wards. On Toan's last stop, he peeked in the operating room; there were still many injured people in the pre-op room and more under the verandah. As he walked to the end of the hallway he encountered a nurse who had stepped out of the surgical unit for a break.

She gestured with both hands. "You should have been here last Wednesday. Ms. Nga and Sister Hai Thanh came marching into the hospital with an armed Viet Cong to take over the hospital."

Toan stared at her in disbelief.

The nurse continued as she told him about a large number of wounded that had been sent there from Long Thanh. She was breathing really hard, her chest heaving as though gasping for air. "We have so many South Vietnamese soldiers, the communist fighters and civilians here. . . ." Her voice tailed off. She shook her head and added, "Dr. Tran was the only physician in town."

Bien Hoa

June, 1975

It was a beautiful June morning. Toan was riding his bicycle to the hospital. Most days he found this ride to be enjoyable. He could stop along the way to pick up some rice then stop by his favorite coffee vendor just before getting to the hospital. Still, he missed his car, which he had sold the previous month. The cost of operation had become too great in the new economy of Vietnam, so he found a buyer who gave him two taels of gold. It was beyond top dollar, plus it allowed him to put the gold away for some big future expense. The gasoline supplies were limited, and Toan believed that the Northern rulers preferred their people to have limited mobility. It was another way of repression and control.

On this morning he sat a little longer eating his rice and fish sauce. He was more melancholy than usual, glancing around at the hustle and bustle of people along the street. That part had almost returned to what he remembered before the fall. His family's lives in the unified Vietnam were starting to take form. He bought Nha-Y a bicycle to ride to her high school teaching job. Their children were back in school where Nha-Y stressed them to excel. Quynh Hoa was at Ngo Quyen High School—not the same school where Nha-Y taught— Vu was at Nguyen Du Elementary and Quynh Dao was at St. Paul's school. Even the hospital was nearly at full staff with several doctors, dentists, and pharmacists having returned to work. No one was overworked, as they had been over the past month.

Toan looked down at his watch. It was time to move along, report to the hospital. He remounted his bicycle and started off the last few blocks. *When would they be getting the latest new demand from the Military Executive Commission? It seems like at least once a week something is being demanded, disguised as a request. The only thing he could give them credit for was giving Dr. Duc a certificate of citation for all operations he performed on the wounded.*

He walked into the outpatient area and was greeted by Dr. Nguyen Thanh Tung. *How unusual. Normally, I beat him to the hospital.* He felt so bad for the man. The State had had it in for him for some unknown reason. *Even last month, Ms. Nga had to take up for him to get him reassigned to the hospital.* They chatted casually for a few minutes, while they looked over the charts of the patients in the waiting area. They split the six patients up and started off to the rooms.

When Toan was finishing with his seventh patient of the morning, he started to walk out of the hospital to get a cup of coffee. As he was passing behind the receptionist, she spun around, looking sad. She handed him the latest communique from the Military Executive Commission. He shook his head as he started to read. This was the one he had dreaded the most. It was about re-education camps. He walked over to the nearest chair and sat down to absorb all it said. The ex-military at the hospital and former chief of service were ordered to go for re-education. Certain students were to go to re-education camps as well, and they should bring clothing and other necessities for one month. *One month.*

The professionals list was more concerning. Besides the newly assigned Dr. Tung, it included two physicians, Dr. Kham and Dr. Duc, and three pharmacists. They were all to be sent to Long Thanh camp, except for Dr. Duc, who was to be sent to another location to be assigned later. *Why?*

When he got to the bottom of the communique, he breathed a great sigh of relief. He was among a group of four physicians exempt from going to re-education. They cited Toan's case as the most unique. He was considered a civil servant of the former administration, a *nguy,* since he was discharged from the army in 1966 before the U.S. was directly involved in the Vietnam conflict. He was greatly relieved. He'd heard about conditions in some of these camps, where the detainees were not fed and had to eat bugs to survive.

Chapter Six

Adjusting to Life under Communist Rule

Saigon

August, 1975

The Vuong family had struggled to visit Nha-Y's parents since selling the Opel. When they finally were able to get there, they stayed late even though it was Sunday and they had to be back to work and school early. It had been more than two months since they'd last visited, and they did not know when they would get back. Toan and the Judge stepped outside to visit with a few neighbors at their homes around the complex, but no one wanted to meet in the common grounds anymore out of fear of repercussions from the revolutionary government. The Judge had become very careful, being a former government and military official. He believed "the walls had ears" and did not trust every one of his neighbors. The wrong word or phrase could get him a stay at a re-education camp.

After their brief visits, they returned to the living room to sitting by themselves. From the seats they could hear the commotion in the kitchen as Nha-Y, the kids, and their grandmother Bao played a very loud game of some kind. Judge Pham seemed to be relaxing into his favorite easy chair, closing his eyes for a minute. Toan thought he might be falling asleep. After a deep breath the Judge asked, "What's been the fallout at the hospital after your interview with the newspaper?"

Toan had anticipated the conversation would eventually get around to this subject. After all, a local interview got republished in the Saigon newspapers. "I thought the interview went well. I went out of my way to flatter the new government. Plus, it was conducted in the presence of a Viet Cong agent, Ms. Nga. Somehow, I was misquoted about my salary. I was saying that everyone was glad to be back to work and happy with the recent upgrades at the hospital. But the person who reported asked about my salary being higher than the hospital director then misquoted me, saying I asked to have my salary lowered. What I said was that we were quite well as our salaries were unchanged. However, it got twisted around somehow that I stated that my salary was higher than the hospital director's . . . Dr. Hai Bon."

The Judge folded his arms across his chest. "My son, you better be careful doing any interviews or answering any questions in public. Changes are coming and they are coming fast."

Toan took his words to heart. "Yes, I learned a very valuable lesson."

The Judge leaned forward in the chair to speak and be heard over the ruckus coming from the kitchen. "Le Duan and the northern leaders of the Vietnam Communist Party are picking up momentum. They move to quash any potential political opponents. They are afraid of any counter-revolutionary insurgency led by the former government or U.S. CIA operatives." He paused for a moment, and jutted his jaw. "First, they sent the military to the re-education camps. Now they have done the same to former civil servants, capitalists. Soon it may well be some Catholic priests and other representatives of the 'old order.' You yourself have witnessed this at the hospital. The noose will continue to tighten."

Toan sat quietly, pondering his words. "What role do you think President Ton Duc Thang plays in this crackdown?"

The Judge sat back in his chair with a big belly laugh. "Thang is a puppet, just like Ho Chi Minh was a puppet at the end of his reign. Le Duan runs the show and the Soviets are pulling his strings, too. He knows if he doesn't rule with an iron fist he'll be gone." He folded his hands on his chest. "If you look at Moscow, you will see how we will live."

Toan had not viewed the deteriorating situation in that way, but clearly his father-in-law had thought it out and had it right.

"Are you afraid they're going to do something with you? I mean, you were part of the civil servants and a military judge."

By the look on the Judge's face, Toan could tell he had asked himself the same question.

"All of these people," the Judge said, "were sent there without criminal charge, trial, or sentence. The word I have from good sources, the communists intend to leave them in the re-education process until the hard labor is done."

Toan interrupted again. "What do you mean *hard labor done*? I thought this was all about brain washing."

"Oh, that's not what they'll say. They'll say it's until the State is satisfied with rehabilitation. But mark my word, this is about revenge and hard-labor projects. These poor people are doing very dangerous jobs. I hear some of our military are heavily involved in minefield sweeping . . . at great risk. All of this with very little food and virtually no medicine."

Nha-Y strolled into the room, still giggling, with the children in tow. It got very loud in the room with their presence. "We need to get home before it gets dark."

Toan acknowledged his wife's comments as he looked at the Judge. Nodding, he got up. Thanh came running over to him, and he hugged her.

As he was walking toward the door with his family, Judge Pham asked, "How bad did the currency exchanges affect you? It had to hit you really hard. Are you still doing okay financially?"

Toan looked back at the Judge. "We are doing okay, better than most." He did not want to tell his father-in-law that his salary had taken a huge hit. He did not want to sound like a complainer when others had it much worse. "Having my private practice shut down has had the biggest impact."

Then his father-in-law stepped from the front door and said, "If you need help, just let us know. Okay?"

Everyone squeezed into his sister Minh's Volkswagen Beetle to drive back to Bien Hoa. He thought about the Judge's question about finances. The currency re-set had been a devastating blow to the wealthy in South Vietnam, as the "revolutionary" government only allowed families to bring in 100,000 dong at most, nothing more.

While Toan's mind was still wrapped up in the question from his father-in-law, Nha-Y inquired, "Why didn't you tell Father what this revolution has done to us? I hate the communists!"

Toan glanced at her, but before he could speak, she continued. "Obviously, Father knows we have been hurt. He wanted you to talk about it."

"I didn't want to sound ungrateful. There are so many people here who have been financially destroyed." His eyes went back on the road. After a brief pause, he continued. "I just didn't want to whine about our situation. We'll be okay."

Toan stopped talking and slowly shook his head. *The devastating rules from the North set up on the first exchange; 500 South Vietnamese dong nets you 1 North Vietnamese dong.* Toan licked his dry lips.

"Some of the doctors at the hospital told me about friends who committed suicide due to what had been taken from them . . . wealth and lifestyle." He paused then added, "You know, if we didn't have friends at the hospital with whom we made financial exchange deals, we too would have been financially destroyed. We still have some money set aside for a rainy day.

Chapter Seven

Double Agent Spy

Bien Hoa

March, 1976

Toan was sitting in a mandatory hospital meeting with a speaker from the north. The speaker was chronicling all the changes in the South, including the country's new name, the Socialist Republic of Vietnam. Saigon was now Ho Chi Minh City, and street names were being changed. *I'll never call Saigon Ho Chi Minh City.* He spun around as the lights went down, and a spotlight lit the area behind where he was standing. A banner slowly unfurled, revealing the new name of the hospital, Dong Nai. As the lights came up again, everyone knew they were to clap for the new name, and most did.

The speaker was not finished. The "revolutionary" government was re-organizing the hospital, he said, yet again.

This was a followup to a remodeling project in Obstetrics. The speaker introduced all the new clinicians, all from the North and all proud members of the Communists Party. Toan looked down at his watch. *When was this meeting going to end?*

He sat at this same table as Dr. Tu Mui, who seemed to be completely uninterested to anything being said by the speaker. The next topic was the new assignments for the staff. The speaker went through the list. "Dr. Khoi will be the new chief of outpatients." Toan knew he was going to be on the move. *Where to?* The speaker droned on. "Dr. Vuong, you are being transferred to internal medicine."

In another fifteen minutes, the meeting was over. People flurried toward the exit, everyone hustling to get out of the small, hot and muggy auditorium.

As Toan walked down the hallway, all he could think about was cleaning out another work area and moving again. However, he was happy with his new assignment. Just then, one of the nurses grabbed his arm from behind. She pulled him aside and exclaimed, "Did you notice that the ever-present Ms. Nga was not sitting on the stage with the speaker?"

Toan hadn't given it any thought at the time. "Why, yes, I guess I did notice, now that you mention it."

Just then Dr. Mui bumped into Toan as he stomped down the hallway and turned into the coffee break room used by the visiting Australian staffers. Toan was taken aback that the woman did not even attempt to apologize for his rude behavior, but the nurse got her attention back with her next comment.

She leaned closer and whispered, "Ms. Nga and her husband, you know Tu Minh, who was chief of the Bien Hoa security service, were put in prison for being spies for the U.S. Central Intelligence Agency."

He could not believe what he'd just heard. It was too much to process. *Ms. Nga a CIA spy. So, she had spied on the Viet Cong or did this have to do with her husband?* He gently pushed himself away from the nurse and slowly continued down the hallway. He knew Ms. Nga's story well. Never in a million years could he imagine her or her husband being spies for the U.S. As he shuffled by the coffee break room, he stopped in his tracks when he overheard Dr. Tu Mui's voice bellow out, "And also that damn Dr. Vuong and nurse Yen, *they* were very close *to that damn Nga. . . . Watch them closely."*

Naturally, these words made Toan very anxious. *Who was he talking to?* As he tried to sort out what the nurse had told him, he reasoned that if Ms. Nga and her husband had really been arrested it was more likely over the "revolutionary" government's latest policy. They were now conducting an internal purge of members of the National Liberation Front. *The evil Le Duan was putting his own harsh stamp on the country. More repression, more human examples. I guess some of the Viet Cong weren't communist enough for them.* That said, he decided to be more aware of who might be watching him. *Damn that Dr. Mui! She had no right to make such an irrational statement about me.*

Chapter Eight

Lack of Medical Supplies

Bien Hoa

Fall, 1976

Toan was reading charts and finishing up his morning rounds in the meningitis ward. While reading the chart at the first bed, Toan was asked by the nurse assisting in that room if he was aware that Dr. Tran Van Duc had returned to the hospital that day. Toan was very happy to have his old colleague back. The poor man had spent almost a full year at a re-education camp. With the recent one hundred percent growth of the hospital, now up to five hundred beds, they desperately needed another senior member in the surgical unit. A few doctors had been transferred in from the region and new doctors were added from the medical school in Saigon, which Toan still refused to call Ho Chi Minh City.

This growth had only added more stress to Toan's life. Because of his excellent work performance in the internal medicine area, he was assigned the additional responsibility of the intensive care department for both men and woman. Then he was added to the inmates' ward. Plus, he was often called in to consult on difficult cases and serious emergencies. To say the least, he was stretched thin. Having a seasoned doctor like Duc back would likely benefit both him and the hospital.

He walked over to another patient in the ward, glanced over his chart. The man desperately needed ten million IU of penicillin. Toan looked at the accompanying nurse and asked, "Did we get any new supplies this morning?"

She only looked down, shook her head and spoke softly. "No, Dr. Vuong."

Toan looked at her as he ordered her to get this patient one million IU of penicillin. The man was in terrible shape and would be lucky to make it through the day.

With a grim look on her face, she nodded. "Yes, Doctor."

He handed her the chart with his initials by the penicillin order, turned and walked out of the room. He wanted to try to find Dr. Duc, just to catch up and welcome him back.

As he paced the hallway, he heard some loud talking down an adjoining hallway ahead and maybe heard his old colleague's voice. Turning the corner, he saw several nurses talking to the doctor. Toan joined the group listening to Dr. Duc. Apparently, he had not noticed Toan walk up. When he did finally notice Toan, the two men greeted each other. Toan asked, "Do you have a minute to talk?"

Dr. Duc just smiled, grabbed Toan's arm and the two men walked off. Toan led him outside to a coffee vendor. Each man grabbed a cup and sat down on a bench where they could talk privately. Toan began giving him a breakdown of the hospital situation. First, he started out describing how many new hospital beds had been added, then he elaborated on the lack of quality medicine.

"To complicate matters," he said, "the pharmacy is controlled by Mr. Cay, who came from the North. All of the pharmacists I worked with in the past have been transferred to other places."

Toan neglected to mention his brother, Can, was also assisting in the pharmaceutical laboratory. He drew a deep breath to tell him the last bit of bad news.

"Because of the order from the Ministry of Health, the pharmacy was ordered to produce IV fluids of poor quality for in-patient use. Disposable needles and tubes have been boiled and re-used tens of times, which makes antisepsis more possible."

With that, Dr. Duc looked at his half a cup of coffee. "We better get back to work before the communists come out to draw and quarter us."

Toan half-smiled at the sarcastic comment. Both men fully knew that there may be some form of punishment if they dawdled too long.

When his day at the hospital had ended, Toan went home, not to relax but to see some old patients, very discreetly. He was a doctor, sworn to the Hippocratic oath. He could not leave them unattended. He saw them on the side and charged them one dong each—if they had it. Many of his patients he did not even charge, the ones he could tell were struggling to get by financially. Toan had decided he could not abandon his former patients just because the government said he could not practice private enterprise. Plus, it was a small way to supplement his income, since the new officially unified government ordered another money exchange. The new currency issued by the North allowed for an exchange rate: For every four South Vietnamese dong, they would receive five new dong. Each family was only allowed to receive up to 200 dong. The cost of living had risen a little more than twenty-five percent in the past year alone, if one could even find the staples one sought. Obviously, the repression of the country's citizens continued. Equality under communism, as applied, was designed to bring everyone down, not raise them up.

As he peddled his bicycle home through the hot and humid evening, he wondered if Dr. Hai Bon knew he was practicing medicine on the side. Certainly, nothing had been said. Over a short period of time, he had earned the respect of the new hospital administration, particularly Dr. Hai Bon. Had this been why they recently increased his income about ten dong a day? Or was it the added responsibilities? Whichever it was, it had placed a heavy burden on him, since he lacked the adequate medical products to help his patients.

As he stepped off the bicycle and pushed it inside, he was met by his first patient, a destitute elderly man who had been with him for almost a decade. The fall to the communists had wiped the elderly gentleman out. He was having extreme abdominal pain. As Toan was beginning his examination, Vu came in from school, sat down opposite his father, and watched him pronounce his diagnosis. He told the elderly man what medicine he would need. Toan walked out of the room. Vu remained seated; he knew exactly what his father was up to. After a brief moment, Toan returned with a small bottle and sat down on the edge of the chair beside the old man. Vu watched intently as his father reached out his hand holding the bottle.

"You're going to be fine. Take one of these pills twice a day, once in the morning and one in the evening with some food. You will feel better within a couple of days. If not, come back and see me. Okay?"

The elderly gentleman looked down as he took the bottle and bowed slightly.

Vu looked at the elderly man, who was clearly experiencing a wave of relief, despite only being diagnosed and without taking a single pill. His father's words had done wonders for the man. Despite having seen that over and over, it never failed to make a positive impression of the power of his father, the doctor's words. He thought, *I want that power some day.*

Toan helped the elderly gentleman to the front door. The old man smiled at Vu and Toan as he walked out. Toan was pleased he could still help his old patients. He was grateful he had been able to make several connections with individuals who could provide him with drugs he so desperately needed to treat patients, even though the drugs were from black-market sources, like all his other drugs. *It was good to have trustworthy contacts.* As long as he continued to be discreet, he did not think he'd get in trouble with the authorities, he just wanted to help his patients.

After the one-hour morning staff meeting, Toan was asked to follow Dr. Hai Bon for a private meeting. *What could this be about? Am I going to get in trouble over my private practice? Buying drugs from the black market? Oh, no. I bet he wants to know what my relationship was with Ms. Nga.*

When he stepped into his office, before he could even sit down, the hospital director tossed some papers at him. Toan nervously picked them up and immediately realized this wasn't about him. He was looking at Dr. Duc's résumé. As Toan straightened the three pages, Dr. Hai Bon pounded his fist on the table. "I want you to review that damn résumé."

Toan leaned over the desk and tapped the pages into their final place as he looked at the director. The man's face was flushed, his jaw clenched as he spoke. "Would you go find Dr. Duc and tell him he only has two choices: One, he is to re-write the CV, or, two, it is back to the re-education camp."

Toan thought it best to get out of this office as fast as possible, before other subjects came up. He hustled himself out.

Was the new Vietnamese government questioning Duc's role in the war? He went to his work area and sat down to read. It became readily apparent what the problem was: Dr. Duc had put together a nicely laid out, well prepared, a very accurate CV. And that was the problem. Toan quickly focused in on the points of Dr. Hai Bon's ire:

> Location of the re-education place: K-9 camp
>
> Time of re-education: 11 months
>
> Status: POW
>
> Charge: I had been working with the government, helping the Australian team, was sent to study abroad, had been served one small meal every three days, one big meal every five days; I committed a crime to save soldiers' lives permitting them to return to fight the revolutionaries.
>
> Demand: I asked to stop operating as I am allergic to anesthetics.
>
> Expectation: I asked to be back to my hometown to tend cattle.

Toan contemplated those harshly accurate statements. He knew Dr. Duc was not allergic to anesthetics, despite his request to cease operating. Plus, he knew there was no way he really wanted to go back to his hometown to tend to cattle.

Toan knew Dr. Duc's background story and the new government was upset. The doctor noted he had worked for the South Vietnamese government. Worse yet, he had committed a crime "to save soldiers' lives, permitting them to return to fight the revolutionaries." He had been treated very poorly and wanted to strike back, which he did with the pen. The "revolutionaries" did not care for his penmanship.

Toan sat back in his chair for a moment and thought about this situation. *Was Dr. Hai Bon testing him? Why did he want me to deliver this message to Dr. Duc? After all, he was the hospital director, not me.*

Toan went to get Dr. Kham to go along with him to talk to Dr. Duc. He showed him the CV, then he had to beg and plead with Dr. Kham to accompany him. Finally, he agreed. Both men cornered Dr. Duc, telling him they wished to speak privately with him. When they went and sat down, Toan spoke, "Dr. Hai Bon wants you to re-write the CV? Please do it for your sake. He said you have two choices—rewrite it or go back to re-education camp."

Dr. Duc defiantly responded as he pounded his fist: "I only told the truth!"

Toan and Dr. Kham nodded in agreement, but Dr. Kham pleaded. "We need you here at the hospital. You are by far our best surgeon. The patients that come in here need you. Please, reconsider making the changes to appease the government. We could all be punished for this."

Toan tried to lighten the mood. "You don't seriously want to go herd cattle, do you?

Dr. Duc snatched the paper from the desk and said, "I'll think about it." Quickly, he exited the area.

The next day, as Toan was making his morning rounds, between rooms he saw Dr. Duc coming up the hallway waving some papers. Toan walked up and met him.

Dr. Duc whispered, "My wife and I talked about this all last night. She said she couldn't handle it if I had to go away to one of those damn camps again. I must do this for her." Dr. Duc held up the papers. "So, will you help me re-write this?"

Toan smiled; it was important to have such a man and a doctor on staff. "I'd be happy to help you." He looked at his watch. "I'm due for a break in about an hour. Meet me in the lunch room then, we'll get that taken care of. You made the right choice."

Dr. Duc forced a half smile and walked away, mumbling, "I'll be there."

Toan could tell how difficult a decision this was for a very proud man. He was relieved—the hospital would retain their senior surgeon.

Plus, it would also benefit Dr. Duc. In the last few weeks, the revolutionary government issued an edict that any surgeon who operated on more than two hundred major cases in a month would receive five xu for every extra case. *Dr. Duc usually operates on three hundred cases per month,* he thought, *therefore, his bonus was enough to pay for a bowl of beef soup for each surgery over two hundred.*

Toan rubbed the top of his head. *How did we get to this situation?*

Then Toan thought of his own predicament. Over the past year, he had conducted several studies and prepared write-ups for the provincial newspapers on the latest patient illnesses. The most common illnesses dealt with fish poisoning, typhoid fever, and insecticide intoxication, most often parathion, plus a few other minor ones. He received five dong for each article. He rested his chin in his hand with his elbow on the arm of his chair. He thought back to his study of parathion poisoning; the insecticide was quite easy to get as it was widely used to eradicate pests. Most often those who became ill from the insecticide were either cultivators who inhaled the insecticide or children who had it applied on their skin as treatment of scabies. He had purposely left out of his article that nine out of ten ER patients had used it to attempt to commit suicide. It was cheap and lethal, only one or two teaspoons of the poison were needed for success. He leaned back on the wooden chair at his desk. *What has happened to my world? We were once a proud people.*

Chapter Nine

Vacation in Da Lat

Mid 1977

It was very early in the morning. The hospital had been slow that night and into the wee hours of morning. Toan laid down on a gurney in the x-ray area. An ER nurse jerked back the curtain, startling him awake. Three patients had just come into the ER with severe vomiting and diarrhea. He got up and followed her around the corner to their waiting room.

His patients were an old woman and her two grandchildren. He asked the elderly woman, "Tell me what you ate and fed to your grandchildren."

The woman looked Toan straight in the eyes. "We were so hungry and could not find anything we could afford, so we ate eggfruit seed until we were full."

He turned to the attending nurse as he shook his head and whispered, "They had to know that was very toxic." He raised his voice to normal levels, so the elderly lady would know she was going to be okay. "Admit them, we'll get them detoxed."

He picked up their charts and wrote on them and handed them to the nurse, who nodded and walked out of the room. Toan followed her and stood beside her outside.

"We will continue to see this situation now," he said. "Either lack of food or lack of money."

He knew the hospital had recently had at least one death from malaria and another that had died from malnutrition. He looked at his watch; his shift was coming to an end. As he walked out of the facility, daylight was just breaking in the eastern sky. He sat on his bicycle enjoying the early morning splendor for an extra minute before starting to peddle off toward home.

When he entered his home, it was very still. No one was up yet. He went and sat in his first floor office. He was surprisingly wide awake after a full night of on-call duty. *I have not written in my journal in a long time. I have a lot of catching up to do and with everyone in the house still in bed perhaps this is the time.*

He opened his latest journal; it had been about two years since his last entry. Then he reached for his oldest journal. How ironic! It started with his youth in Hanoi running from the re-occupation of the French. He leafed through the pages for a while, scanning stories about his family and the old times. Seeing those writings, he became melancholy. After a moment more of reflection, he picked up his most recent journal and began to write his thoughts:

> Since the communists have taken over, Dong Nai Hospital has seen many changes, a few for the good but most not so. The situation only continues to deteriorate. Medication and medical supplies are depleting rapidly. Simple items such as cotton, bandages, IV tubes, etc. Where should they go to fill these needs? Often the black market. Sometimes, even the patients have had to reach out to the black market. Lastly, I, myself, could not keep my private practice open without that same black market.
>
> To make matters worse, almost all drugs now imported from the USSR were spoiled. Most small medical appliances were supplied by East Germany and they were inferior. IV fluids were still produced by local pharmacies, but they are not

up to previous standards. The East Germans were importing raw materials from some Western European countries, but they did not flow smoothly into the country. Most countries are still unwilling to help the communist country.

Then just in the last few weeks, it was not uncommon for the tuberculosis ward to report one death every week due to the patients not getting enough to eat or receiving the essential treatment. The staff was incredibly heart-broken to look after moribund patients; as a clinician, I was deeply disturbed when I let a comatose diabetic patient die for lack of insulin or a patient with meningitis die because of a lack of penicillin.

The hospital is not beyond strange cases, like the department of surgery receiving a patient who had been injured by his neighbor. He had sustained cleaver wounds after stealing some cassava plants. The police ordered the neighbor to pay the victim's treatment.

To illustrate yet another idiosyncrasy at the hospital: The old staff was ordered to write all medical records in Vietnamese. I bought a medical dictionary printed in the North to use. However, the new physicians, who ironically transferred in from the North, wrote their records in French. It was as though they were proud to know French. The same French who had kept Vietnam a repressed colony for more than a century.

The Dong Nai hospital working schedule remained unchanged. Staff hours were from eight to five for six days a week, Sundays off. However, many were required to labor at Long Thanh or be on-call those days. Salaries were terrible for those physicians who graduated after 1977. Plus, the starting probation salary was 85% of that of a first-grade physician, or $51 a month. If they lived in Saigon and had to take a train to go to the hospital, it cost $2 round trip. How can they expect these physicians to make it financially?

Privately, I am beginning to question the qualifications of some of the physicians sent down from the North. Over the years, many medical schools in the North had to move or shut down to avoid the bombing from French or American aircrafts. Some physicians from Bung graduated from medical school in the jungle or in Hanoi. Dr. Cac of the pediatric department claims she is a de-facto doctor as she had attended classes and graduated from the medical school in Hanoi. Many nurses learned to become alternate physicians before becoming doctors. I did some private investigation of Dr. Sau An, the man who replaced Dr. Hai Bon as director of the hospital for the first five months of this year. By his own words, he only got to the 3rd grade but by the grace of Big Uncle—the North's favorite name for Ho Chi Minh—and that of the Revolutionary Party, he became a nurse then he was sent to learn to be an alternate physician then a doctor. It is really better to be Red than a specialist.

Dr. An has just been transferred back to Ho Nai hospital as the director. They sent Dr. Hai Bon to return to his role as the director of the hospital. Upon his return, he announced that the government said that, beginning this summer, everyone could take a one-week vacation. Needless to say, Nha-Y was thrilled. Now I have to be able to afford it.

Since they were all hospital staff, they were able to purchase necessities for daily living at a rationed price, usually ten to twenty percent of actual market prices. Still, most had to buy more than their rationed provisions. Staff and dependents were permitted to buy thirteen kg's of rice and thirty cc's oil each month. Every once in a while, my staff and I could afford to purchase a few hundred grams of meat or fish, but it was often spoiled, and the rice was moldy. Occasionally, several hundred gms of sugar could be purchased. Sweetened condensed milk was rationed to one can every three months for three individuals; the milk was produced from coconut milk. Once a year, during the Tet festival, the hospital staff ordered pigs slaughtered to sell meat to workers. Each person could buy one-half kg of pork.

To make my point, I was told about several of the doctors living in a villa at Cong Ly Street in Bien

Hoa. They put wooden boards under the staircase to shelter a newborn pig they bought. Every week workers who were forced to labor in the fields at Long Thanh chopped banana trees to give them food for the pig. At the same time, Dr. Nhan used to get the debris of the fetus and placenta when she did a D & C (abortion) to feed the pig. By the end of the year, they sold their fattened pig and received enough money to pay their expenses for the Tet festival.

The news about the country really is not any better. From the beginning of the year, there has been diplomatic trouble brewing between Vietnam and Kampuchea, which we all have known as Cambodia. Publicly, both countries attempted to act as if relations were good, but this was not true. In order to attempt to control the Indochina peninsula, the Red Chinese became a close ally of Kampuchea after Vietnam chose to maintain its ties with the Soviet Union, its main ally during the Vietnam Conflict.

In the middle of April, the Kampuchean revolutionary army seemed to be preparing for military actions against Vietnam. On Kampuchea's second anniversary, Vietnam sent a congratulatory message. When everything looked as though the situation was calming down, the Chinese decided it was time to "teach Vietnam a lesson." They sent troops to invade Lang Son, which they later withdrew.

Here is where things get weird. While the Vietnamese agents praise the Vietnamese-Chinese friendship out of one side of their mouth, out of the other side they put Vietnamese-Chinese on a watch list so they can be followed by police. The Vietnamese government initiated a policy to expel the Chinese-Vietnamese from Vietnam.

Despite still being in Catholic schools, the children's education has really dipped since the North took over. It's the same teachers but cirriculum has changed. Schools are re-education camps for the children. They are forced into the Red Youth, based on the Chinese Red Guard. Yet,

> they are taught about Red China's expansion policies. Once a week, speakers are set up. They play propaganda audios and hold parades, complete with the children expected to be out there waving flags of the new Vietnam. This is difficult to accept.

Toan could hear noises upstairs, it sounded like Nha-Y and the children were up. He quickly read back over what he had written. *I need a conclusion. I have got to try to keep up with my journal.*

He wrote:

> I believe that Le Duan and President Thang have created the dispute so that they could proclaim many of them were Chinese agents, thus having an opportunity to seize personal riches.

With the journal entry complete, he went to be with his family. After breakfast, he wanted to smoke a cigarette and lay down to get some rest. When he got to the top of the steps, Nha-Y greeted him with a cup of coffee. This brought a smile to his face. His beautiful wife and a cup of coffee—what could be better?

When Toan sat down at the breakfast table, he discovered Nha-Y had an ulterior motive. She wanted to talk about planning some kind of vacation. She reminded him they had not had a vacation for several years. As she was making her case, Toan could say nothing because he wanted to take some time off, too. However, Dr. Hai Bon, who only just returned as director of the hospital, had not even set up the procedures and the seniority chart. Toan knew he would be near the top.

The next day, Toan ran into Ms. Long, a former patient and a vender at the city market. As they were having a light conversation, the subject of his family vacation came up; he and his wife were undecided about where to go on. Ms. Long suggested that he and his wife should go to Da Lat. Her argument was quite persuasive. Two things emerged from their conversation: One, he would like to visit the romantic city one more time where they had spent their honeymoon in 1963; and two, he could buy products to re-sell and to get some extra money.

Toan and Nha-Y left three of their four children at Nha-Y's parents but took Vu with them. The Palace hotel, where they had honeymooned, was reserved exclusively for government officials, so they could not stay at that hotel. Instead, they stayed at a small, untidy hotel. During short walks, they observed the changes to Da Lat since 1963; now, it was sparsely populated. Moreover, few regular citizens could afford to travel to the resort town, therefore, the streets were mostly deserted. It was hardly like their honeymoon fourteen years earlier: no beautiful hotel, no dreamy Xuan Huong Lake, no drives visiting gorgeous landscapes surrounding the city, and certainly no French cuisine for dinner. They were able to have meals at the market and visited the Cam Ly waterfall.

On their next to the last day in Da Lat, Toan and Nha-Y decided to see if they could find a large quantity of coffee, tea, some exotic fruit and any other items to take back to Bien Hoa and sell for some extra money. It was for this very reason Vu was brought on the trip because he was vigorous and had the "street smarts" to find the "black markets" of Da Lat.

Vu and Toan stood and talked for a moment. Vu told his father to walk a good way behind him as he worked his way up the busy commercial street. He would talk to other young boys to see if he could find anyone who was connected to the black market. If he got a good tip, he would signal his mother and father by sitting down on the street and taking off one sandal. They would approach and the three of them would go together to the market.

Vu set out ahead, periodically stopping and talking to boys, asking along the busy streets to find the right proprietors. Vu stopped several young Vietnamese before finally finding a young boy who stopped and talked to him for a few minutes. Vu looked back at his parents; they stopped and pretended to window-shop at a clothing vendor establishment. When the two boys finished talking, Vu started walking again but stopped after about a half a block and sat down and took off his sandal. He waited for his parents to catch up. He stood back up and said, "At the edge of the commercial market area, the third from the last on the right is owned by an old man who sells just about anything you want, from illegal drugs to coffee."

Toan looked at Nha-Y, who nodded in approval. Toan said, "Take Vu and walk back up the street a couple of blocks. I'll go find the owner, pick up the items, and come back and meet you."

As he walked up the street, Toan began to get nervous about his risky venture. When he saw several men standing close enough to see the business Vu had described, he stopped dead in his tracks. *Could they be undercover constables? They have to be, just waiting to pounce on any activity.*

Toan turned around and quickly walked back to find his wife and son. When he rejoined them, he told them the story. Vu offered to go back and check it out but Toan thought better of it. He wasn't about to take any chances.

So in the end, Toan and Nha-Y purchased only a small quantity of fruit, some tea, and a little coffee. They had no intention of re-selling any of these cherished items.

The next day as they were about to board the bus for the trip back to Bien Hoa, two constables stopped them and searched them for contraband. The constables went through all their belongings only find the small quantities they had purchased and it was very tense for a few minutes. They harassed Toan, Nha-Y, and Vu for a few minutes. It was good they had not purchased any large quantities of goods.

Late June, 1977

Toan continued to operate his private medical practice, very much on the QT, from the first floor of his home. As far as the government was concerned it was closed. However, Toan's Hippocratic oath would not allow him to turn away his patients. Despite the tightening of the black market medical drug industry, Toan maintained a relationship he had had with a previous pharmacy. It worked out well for both, as the pharmacist had hidden away his supplies for under-the-table resale and for Toan, who wished to maintain his practice. Toan kept a consistent supply of the most often demanded drugs on hand, plus he knew within a few days he could get the more exotic medicine. He had created a nice hiding place behind his own medicine cabinet in their bathroom on the third floor. If the government came looking, they would have to know where to look to bust him. He kept a meticulous inventory of his black market medicines, not only so he would know what he could immediately supply his patients but also because they were not cheap, despite having a friend who sold him the drugs.

Almost two years of operating off the books allowed Toan to improve his family's household budget. So far no one at the hospital made any comments, but some of them had to know. Toan was able to get enough financial security to hire a maid named Ms. Nam. Also, he and his family would go visit his sister Minh and borrow her VW Beetle to drive to Saigon to visit his in-laws and brother Kien. Gasoline was still so expensive that he could only afford to do so occasionally.

For several months, Ms. Nam came in and took care of almost all the daytime chores. Up until that time, no one bothered Toan's hidden medical supplies. Then Toan began to notice things disappearing from his inventory. His records were as they had always been—meticulously detailed. He sat down at his desk late one afternoon and reviewed his list to make sure he had not made any mistakes, reviewing several times his list of patients and what he had supplied. Everything matched except his inventory. He trusted every single one of his family, as they all knew how important his patients were to him. He reasoned the only variable was Ms. Nam. His records had been accurate up until her employment. Had she found his supplies? But how? He wanted to be sure.

One afternoon he set a trap that only she could fall into—if she was the guilty party. Early that morning before she showed up for work, he verified his supplies. When he returned after a day at the hospital, sure enough, valuable drugs were missing. Nha-Y knew of his plan and the children had been at school all day. Toan confronted Mrs. Nam immediately. She did not deny she had taken them and left the minute the subject was brought up.

Chapter Ten

First Escape Attempt

Bien Hoa

December, 1977

Toan was standing at the nurse's station when one of the nurses held up a chart. Toan looked at it then back at her. Without a word, she pointed to the diagnosis on the chart. This brought a smile to his face. One of the new doctors, who had trained in Saigon, was really going to be good. Toan looked at the nurse and half-jokingly said, "If students from abroad want to become good clinicians, they should come to Vietnam as we get examples of every phase of every disease you can think of."

Toan went around the corner to his office to make morning notes on patients and write some prescriptions. As he was writing, there was a knock on his open door. It was another nurse, and she held out a single piece of paper. As he waved her in, he asked, "What is it?"

"It's from Dr. Hai Bon."

Toan took the piece of paper from her, she turned and walked out. He started reading:

> New policy announcements from Director Doctor Hai Bon's office
>
> Effective immediately, all workers will no longer be required to labor in the fields at Long Thanh. Also, new schedules are as follows: Working hours shall remain unchanged, but on-duty physicians will receive two out of three Sundays off. Internists will still be on call every three days.
>
> Signed: Dr. Hai Bon, Director

Toan smiled. Finally, the revolutionary government has figured out that most hospital workers don't make good farmers. The hospital staff's planting of potatoes and cassava produced a poor harvest despite the produce being sold to workers at the official government price, yet it would only pay for about one tenth of the cost to the hospital staff of gas for transportation. *Most will be happy to give it up because it was a losing proposition.*

Just then there was another knock on his open door. Toan looked up to see his brother, Can, standing there. He was frowning. Toan waved him in. His brother delicately closed the door behind him without a sound, picked up a chair from in front of Toan's desk and moved it over beside him. Toan put his chin in his hand, waiting to hear what his brother wanted to say.

Can leaned over and whispered, "I have a friend who was going to help me escape to one of the foreign countries. Do you want to join me?"

Toan glanced at him then around his office as he thought. He already knew what Nha-Y would say. *No need to ask.* Then he nodded without so much as a word.

Can jumped up and carried the chair back around the desk. "I'll get back when I know more."

Two days later

Toan was standing at the nurse's station reviewing charts when his brother walked by him. Can gave him "the nod" as he walked by. It meant he wanted to meet him in his office. He finished up the chart he was working on then headed that way. A few minutes after he sat down at his desk, Can came by and knocked on his open office door. Toan waved him in.

Can closed the door behind him, sat down and relaxed in the wooden chair for a minute to catch his breath. Then he asked, "Are we sure the walls don't have ears?"

Toan shrugged.

Can dragged the chair around to his side of the desk and whispered into his brother's ear. "You are off this Sunday, right?"

Toan nodded.

Can replied, "Here is what I know. This Sunday, be in by Phuoc Tinh by 5:00 p.m. I'll meet you with my friend."

Toan leaned away and shrugged his shoulders as he frowned. "Okay, but you don't know any more?"

Can got up and started toward the door. "No, it's for both of our safeties." Can smiled at his brother then left.

Toan felt uneasy and anxious, yet at the same time he was excited. He wanted desperately to escape the deteriorating situation at both the hospital and the country as a whole.

When Nha-Y heard what little details there were to the escape plan, she was thrilled. They talked into the night about many things; the excitement kept them from sleeping. Among the things they discussed was whether or not to tell their children, or at least their older children. In the end, they chose not to divulge anything. Instead, they decided only to tell them they were taking them to the beach.

Sunday, January 8, 1978

Toan was finishing his morning cigarette, and as he snubbed it out, he glanced down at his sister's VW Beetle. He'd borrowed it the night before. He told her he wanted to take his family to the beach for the day. He had decided it was best to not tell her the story, as she did not want to escape. While he trusted her, it was best to keep the circle tight around those who knew what was going on.

At the breakfast table, with all the children present, Toan announced they should scurry off and get together some things, as he was going to take them to the beach. The children were excited. They had not been on vacation since the fall of Vietnam. They had only visited their grandparents in Saigon a few times. *I still call it Saigon, always will.* Within a few minutes the five children were running out to their aunt's car to pile in and go off to the little community of Vung Tau.

The drive out of their neighborhood was quiet, but once they started down the main commercial street of Bien Hoa, they passed many residents out walking. All the markets were open. People were moving in and out, purchasing food for their daily meal. Before leaving the city limits, Toan pulled into a gas station and, as usual, overpaid to fill up the fuel-efficient old Beetle.

Nha-Y pointed out the large, half constructed statue of Jesus Christ and turned to the backseat to tell the children they were almost to Vung Tau. She began to tell them the story about the Catholics starting to build the statue before the communists took over but could see the story had little meaning to them. She quit without completing the history lesson.

Toan looked at his watch as they drove into the beach community. It was about noon. The rocky hills seem to come right down to the beautiful light brown sandy beach, which sat back in a cove. After grabbing a quick lunch at a small outdoor restaurant along the beach, Toan and Nha-Y found a place to park, close to the beach, then let the children play on the beach and swim. They took up temporary residence under a very large shade tree and tried to relax as best they could. They enjoyed the sounds of their children playing and small waves lapping on the beach. Nha-Y continued to canoodle over Quynh Trang and Thanh while Toan enjoyed watching the large freighters moving out beyond the bay. The children were having more fun than they had in a couple of years, totally oblivious of what was about to transpire.

As the afternoon passed, Toan and Nha-Y became anxious, even agitated. The children ran back and forth from the beach to where they were under the shade tree. Toan began watching his wristwatch at about 2:30; from that point on, he glanced at it more frequently. At one point, he held it up to his ear to make sure it was still running. He feared asomething would make him late and miss their opportunity to escape.

Once his watch finally reached 4:00 p.m., Toan stepped from the shade, walked down to the surf and ordered his children to go up to the open public showers. They were to wash the saltwater off and change clothes. It was time for them to leave. The children protested, as they were still having so much fun. Toan stood his ground against their brief protests and watched them slowly walk toward the showers. Nha-Y came down to the shoreline and scooped up Thanh to hurry him along. After the children showered themselves off and changed into fresh, dry clothes, they unhappily returned to the car. Toan glanced around at all of them. His look settled them down, and he glanced back at Nha-Y, who winced a brief smile.

Toan looked down at his watch again. Plenty of time to make it to Phuoc Tinh to meet his brother by 5:00 p.m. Then they would get on the boat and escape.

As they approached Phuoc Tinh, the scene was completely different. While there was a beach, Phuoc Tinh was primarily a fishing village. There was a strong smell of fish as they crossed a little bridge and approached a line of fishing boats and a few trawlers. It wasn't as pleasant as when walking into a fish market back in Bien Hoa. Since he had no idea where to find Can, he chose to park along what he had determined must be the main street in town. Huts were scattered among the few buildings. He looked down at his watch, just about 5:00 p.m., the designated time. Toan opened the car door and stepped out. He waved to everyone else to follow suit.

Within a few minutes, everyone was out of the car walking along the street. The more they walked, Toan sensed how perilous their situation had become. Quynh Hoa, Vu, and Quynh Dao exchanged glances with one another as they walked up and down the same street for almost an hour. They hoped they were about going to finally get out of Vietnam. Vu wondered what had taken his parents so long. They had not talked about such a big, important topic, but they all wanted to go to the United States.

The small seashore town was poor, with few houses, and most of its residents were likely fishermen. *We stick out like a sore thumb,* Toan thought. *We are so out of place and the children are starting to get restless from boredom. They are tired and hungry.*

No one came to meet them. *Where is Can?* Conversely, they did not want to give up on their opportunity to escape. Toan whispered to Nha-Y. "Perhaps we should walk farther up the street." He pointed toward an area with more trees and foliage away from the small houses and huts. They would be out of sight of the car and at greater risk should they have to get away fast, but he had to do everything possible to find his brother.

As they got farther away from the huts and small dilapidated houses, a man jumped out from behind a thicket of large overgrown bushes. His actions scared Toan, who quickly pushed his family behind him in an attempt to defend them. Turned out to be his brother, Can, barely recognizable. His face was full of despair as he spoke.

"We failed! The constable had a checkpoint on the way to the sea." Can waved his arms wildly as he continued, "Go back home now to avoid being seized!"

Before Toan could question his brother's gut-punching words, Can turned and was running in the opposite direction, away from the car. Toan wanted—*needed*—more information. He started to pursue his brother. "Wait! Wait!"

After taking two or three running steps, he stopped. His brother was now running hard away from them. Toan could not leave his family unattended to chase him down. He had to protect his family; that was his number one obligation. But he had questions, and he was going to get answers from his brother. Just not now. He had a whole new dilemma. He and his family had no choice but to get out of there and return home. Toan was shocked, but he attempted to hide it as he hustled them back toward the VW Beetle.

They all hurried as fast as they could go, even to the point of now being blatantly obvious. But with two very young children, the pace was much slower than either Toan or Nha-Y desired. *Would the constables be showing up in town at any moment to grab them?* When they finally reach the VW, someone had stolen the headlights. When they looked inside, they saw all their items were gone as well. It was now long after 6:00 p.m. Toan knew there was nothing he could do about it, at least not right now. Still, he had to get his family home. He quickly shuffled everyone inside the Beetle and drove away from the little community.

Toan continued as fast as he could, but nightfall was outrunning him. When it got completely dark, he had no choice but to slow way down. By the time Toan got to Long Thanh, it was totally dark and he could no longer see the road. He had to get his family home somehow. Fortunately, he had a flashlight, which he had Nha-Y pull out and project the light on the roadside. As bad as the flashlight was, it was better than nothing at all. Fortunately for them the road was completely deserted; literally, no traffic at all. They arrived home around 9:00 p.m. Thank God!

Everyone slowly walked into their house. The children were tired from a day of play and riding in the car. Toan and Nha-Y were exhausted and greatly depressed by their failure and their anxious drive home.

Bien Hoa

Monday morning, January 9, 1978

First thing in the morning, as soon as Toan was sure a friend of his was awake, he called. When his friend answered, he asked if he knew anyone who would sell him a couple of VW Beetle headlights. His friend replied he probably did. Let him make some calls and he would get back to Toan shortly. About a half hour later, his friend called back to tell him he found a pair but they were expensive.

Toan's head dropped; one more thing on top of his failure. "It doesn't matter. I was expecting as much." He was just happy he could replace them then return the VW Beetle none the worse for wear as if nothing had happened.

Nha-Y wrote a poem about their experience:

Phùớc Tỉnh

Cách Mạng thành công lo vuọt biên,
Vùa may Phuớc Tỉnh có mối liền!
Anh em một dạ cùng chung hẹn,
Xe 'bug' bảy nguòi liều thủ xem!
Chờ mãi mới hay tàu bể mánh,
Nhìn xe hết viá mất tiên đèn!
Một nhà lập cập trong Đêm tối,
Chồng lái xe mò vợ rọi pin.

Chapter Eleven

The Second Escape Attempt: The Stories of Mr. Chin and Many Others

Dong Nai hospital

January, 1978

Toan emerged from the malaria ward and walked toward his office. Turning the corner in the hallway, he saw Mr. Chin standing in front of his office. *Oh no, not Mr. Chin again. Sometimes, he's just a bother. I sure hope he hasn't been standing out there very long.* Toan waved his arm frantically, pointing him into his office ahead of him. *My association with this man has not helped my situation at all.* Yet Toan was always excited to be brought up to speed on the latest developments. He picked up the pace to his office and stepped inside, closed the door. *I hope this isn't another story to take home to get Nha-Y's hopes up, only to have them dashed.*

He sat down at his desk. Despite his attempt to be kind and considerate to this man, it was becoming more and more difficult. "How long have you been standing there? It is not good to have everyone see you and I associated."

Before Mr. Chin answered, as usual, he set a large bag of coffee on Toan's desk. Toan enjoyed the coffee; he wondered if that was half the reason he was still being kind to the man. Mr. Chin leaned back in the chair and spoke confidently.

"I was successful getting your family registered to leave Vietnam since you have Chinese blood." He folded his arms across his chest and continued. "But the constable contacted me last night with some bad news. After doing their background check, in spite of your Chinese origin, you are a government official. If they permit you to leave, how could they tell the hospital and the health service? So we will not be able to take you this time."

Mr. Chin's news was really disappointing. Toan had pulled a favor from a former Chinese government official and acquired Chinese-Vietnamese identification. Everything had looked on the up and up.

Mr. Chin got up and went to the closed door. "Perhaps we can work out something different in the future."

Toan was not sure whether or not he believed the man. At the end of the previous year, the man told Toan he had purchased two boats, each of which would handle up to 250 people. Toan knew Mr. Chin had money, but he didn't think he had that kind of money. Toan rented his private practice office and home from Chin's mother-in-law. Now, she did have money, big money. She was one of the few to be making it in the new communist world because she owned rental properties, which ensured a constant flow of cash. Despite all of that, it seemed to be taking a long time to get the escape lined up. Toan was worried he had been given the stall treatment and now he was being fed lies.

The accuracy of Chin's story was not his biggest worry. He had a much larger one. How much longer would the Vietnamese government allow the exodus of Chinese citizens? China had just cut ties with Hanoi. At any point in time, he believed Vietnam could stop allowing citizens of Chinese heritage to leave the country. The rift between China and the Soviet Union was widening, Vietnam desperately needed aid and the Soviet Union was the only potential help. Then there is Kampuchea stirring up things with Le Duan. This place is a mess. *Now, I can't escape semi-officially because the government won't let me. I thought I wasn't a government official, which kept me out of the re-education camps, but now I am a government official since I work at this hospital.*

He drew a deep breath and attempted to rationalize the situation the best he could. Maybe this was a positive thing, considering only about one month earlier, Dr. Duc had been registered to leave semi-officially. He and his family had boarded the boat, then constables boarded, called his name, and arrested him and his family. The more Toan thought about it, the more he came to the conclusion that Mr. Chin thought Toan's presence on his boats would affect hundreds of other passengers.

Bien Hoa

Late February, 1978

Toan walked into a local market to pick up a few items for Nha-Y. There he saw Ms. Tam, Mr. Chin's sister-in-law, walking out. She greeted Toan with a smile, then grabbed his arm and walked him back outside. *This is most curious. She has never acted in this manner. She has always been very formal.*

She pointed to a small garden area on the other side of the street. They started across the busy street and no sooner were they several steps off the curb, the traffic light turned green and the thirty or so mopeds all started moving simultaneously. The two of them were now stopping, starting, jogging, dodging between the mopeds, attempting to make it to the other side of the street. The sound of the moped horns was deafening and disorienting. At one point, Toan was certain she was going to drop her small bag of groceries.

Once they reached their destination, the street noise was minimized. Ms. Tam grabbed Toan's hand and flashed a big smile. "I have good news. Both of my brother-in-law's boats made it to Malaysia."

Toan forced a quick half smile, yet at the same time, hearing this bit of news was very frustrating. Ms. Tam looked at him, and her smile changed. "Perhaps in the future I can be of some further assistance to you."

With that, she pivoted and scurried away.

Chapter Twelve

Dr. Duc Returns

Bien Hoa

April, 1978

Toan and Nha-Y were sitting in their living room. It was late in the evening, but Toan knew he had to give his wife time to speak her mind. They often talked about difficult things late, when the children were in bed. Nha-Y had been troubled over the past few days. The news coming out of Kampuchea was only getting worse, and Vu, their oldest son, was approaching military age. Nha-Y looked him in the eyes. "Le Duan continues to send more young boys from the South to Kampuchea out of spite. It is just more punishment he seeks to inflict on us."

Toan knew it was best not to respond or debate her when she was talking about their children. She had their best interests at heart at all times.

Unseen by his parents, Vu heard them talking from the hallway. He had already been asleep, but had awakened very thirsty. He'd started toward the kitchen for some water when he'd heard his parents talking about the possibility of his being drafted and sent to Kampuchea. He'd heard them talk about that for more than a year. Honestly, he paid little attention; he was just fourteen, still two years away from draft age. Seemed like a long time off. He decided it was best to just go back to bed, as his parents would try to pull him into the conversation if he walked past them on his way to the kitchen.

The petite and pretty Nha-Y sat there as determined as ever. "I don't believe for a minute that Vietnam is trying to overthrow the Khmer Rouge because they are killing their own civilians."

Toan was looking for an opening to jump into the conversation and change the subject, but at the moment, it seemed hopeless.

Nha-Y changed the subject on her own, but Toan felt he could not interrupt this topic either because she was still talking about the family when she said, "I can barely feed our family on what the government has allowed us. Now, we are being rationed further. If it weren't for your private practice we would starve to death."

Toan nodded in total agreement, but it was obvious she had a lot of built-up hostility. Something specific had clearly ticked her off. She said, "Why are we still here?"

Toan knew that was his chance to jump in and try to get in a word. "You remember several months ago when Ms. Tam mentioned that Mr. Chin made it to Malaysia? She said then she might be able to offer some assistance some day. Well, I've been thinking of contacting her to see if she meant escape. Perhaps she knows other people? You know how well connected she is."

Nha-Y gave him a stern look, before a brief smile came on her face. "Honey, we must do something. We just can't keep living like this. What kind of legacy are we leaving our children?"

Just then their doggie Ki came running into the living room, dancing around. This was his sign that Toan had to take him out. As he got up and headed toward the door, Nha-Y laughed. "You know you love him, too."

As Toan reached the door, he turned back to her. "Of course, I do. It is just he can be an inconvenience sometimes.

When I get into the office tomorrow, I'll get Ms. Tam's phone number and try to get a meeting with her."

Once he was in the back yard with Ki, he realized while he usually complained about having to take the dog out, he was glad Ki had showed up when he did. It got Toan out of a one-sided conversation.

It was an extra warm, humid morning for Toan's bicycle ride to work. Just a constant reminder of how life had changed. He thought about driving around the city before he was married in his Peugeot convertible with the top down. It seemed like a lifetime ago and it was. By the time he reached his favorite coffee vendor's cart near the hospital, he was sweating profusely. He sat down for a moment under the closest tree to enjoy his morning brew and cool off before checking in at the hospital. It was even too hot to have a cigarette.

As he took the last drink from his cup, he thought about the day he and his father went shopping to buy his wedding gifts. *How I miss my father.* He looked down at his watch. Time to stop daydreaming, get back in the present, go to work. He tossed the empty cup in the trash can, climbed back on his bike and peddled off.

Toan went to the nurse's station to pull the charts, see who was new and get an updated status of the patients he had seen the day before. It would be another day of anguish seeing patients he could cure in a matter of days with the proper medication. That was still so lacking. In his mind he set his order of visits and started down the hallway.

When he turned the corner, he was caught by surprise by a man in a long white medical coat. It was his old colleague, Dr. Duc. This brought a big smile to his face; he moved quickly to greet him. He hadn't expected to see Dr. Duc again. The last Toan had heard, Dr. Duc was in jail for trying to escape this forsaken place and he wanted the whole story. Why had he been imprisoned? It had real relevance to what he and his wife were planning for Toan's own family. The two men agreed to meet up later.

After making his morning rounds, Toan met Dr. Duc coming down the hallway, both men headed for the lunchroom from opposite directions. Toan suggested that they go outside for a cup of coffee, knowing full well they could talk more freely outside. The surgeon agreed. *The outdoors does not have ears like these walls.*

As they walked around the hospital, Toan started the conversation with the usual *how's the family*, then told him about his. After the small talk, each man had finished their coffee and Toan asked, "So tell me what happened on your escape attempt?"

The doctors walked in silence for a few more steps.

"Well first off," Dr. Duc said at last, "I would not be here if it were not for Dr. Hai Bon. I am not so sure he wasn't the one to tip off the constables. You know, just to teach me a lesson. I think he is still mad about my CV. Anyway, he had to go to the authorities and requested my early release, saying the hospital needed me."

Toan nodded affirmatively, while wishing Duc would get to where and how they had been arrested. Dr. Duc continued his story, telling a tale very similar to that of what Toan had almost gone through earlier.

"My family and I registered to leave semi-officially, complete with Chinese papers. Just about the time the boat was ready to push off, constables boarded and called out my name only. When I stepped forward, they grabbed me and my family. They made me stand there and watch the boat leave before they took us away."

His story was gut-wrenching on so many levels; he still wanted to escape but realized everything would have to be just right to get out of Vietnam. Toan agreed with Duc that there was a high probability that the hospital director had been tipped off to Duc's escape attempt and let him sit in prison for a few months to teach him a lesson. Dr. Duc and Dr. Hai Bon were like water and oil, both very strong willed and unrelenting.

Toan walked into his private office and opened the center door to his desk. He pulled out a small piece of paper with Ms. Tam's telephone number. He picked up his phone and dialed the number. When she answered, she agreed to stop by his home as soon as possible to talk.

Toan walked into the same garden spot he had met Ms. Tam several months earleir. Toan had suggested they meet at his home, but Ms. Tam informed him that her contact would not come there. He wanted everything done at arm's length to start. He stood there for a couple of minutes, concerned about being too obvious. Finally, he saw Ms. Tam walking up with another individual. *She's right on time.*

Ms. Tam motioned her hand outward. "This is Mr. Phat. He is a Chinese-Vietnamese and may be able to assist you."

Toan shook the man's extended hand.

"I am Mr. Phat, I live over in Cho Lon."

They stepped away from the busy street. Mr. Phat put his hands on his hips. "Ms. Tam, here, said you are interested in escaping Vietnam. I have organized several 'semi-official' trips so far. I am Chinese-Vietnamese and am organizing another trip soon."

Toan replied, "Yes, my family and I are interested. Very interested."

Mr. Phat remained in his position, then tilted his head. "Your price is going to be twenty-three tael of gold. A large portion must be paid in advance. The balance is due at boarding time."

Toan was taken aback by the man's demands, not to mention he did not have that much gold or any way to obtain it. Toan put on his best poker face and nodded in agreement.

Mr. Phat seemed to study his expression then continued speaking. "Good, good. I will put you in contact with my assistant. His name is Ly. You will be dealing directly with him from this time forward."

Toan could do nothing but nod. "Do you have any timetable?"

Mr. Phat glanced at Ms. Tam, then started to slowly inch away from the meeting. "No, not at this time. Ly will be in touch." With that Mr. Phat started away faster with Ms. Tam following behind. She looked back and shrugged.

Toan was dejected as he went home anticipating what his conversation was going to be like with Nha-Y; they only had six tael of gold and four hundred U.S. dollars at that time. His expectations from their meeting had been much better than the conversation itself, which was nothing short of exasperating.

At home, Toan wanted to avoid Nha-Y, but she came and found him. He related all the conversation with Ms. Tam and her contact. Nha-Y was distraught. She too had much higher expectations, and her rising anger began to emerge as their conversation deteriorated. All Toan could say was, "I don't even own enough assets to purchase the amount of gold needed to pay for our trip."

Nha-Y got up and paced around the living room, looking pensive. Toan watched her and tried to get her to say something, anything. Finally, she sat back down and grabbed Toan's arm. "I will go talk to my parents. See if they can help us."

Toan leaned back into the couch. He understood her anguish, but it was not what he really wanted to do. He was an established doctor. He did not feel it was right to bring his problems to his in-laws.

As soon as Toan was able to arrange to borrow Minh's VW Beetle, the entire family went to Nha-Y's parents' home to visit. After dinner, the children left the table and Nha-Y's mother removed the dishes. Nha-Y turned to her father. "Toan and I desperately need your help."

The look on her father's face changed from relaxed to concerned.

Nha-Y nudged Toan to explain the entire predicament. Once he had completed laying out the story, yet again, he finished with the request to borrow twenty-one tael of gold, adding, "Would you be interested in going with us?"

Pham Gia He shook his head no.

Before he could speak, Nha-Y spoke first. "Father, are you sure you don't want to try to escape with us?"

Nha-Y's father looked up at his wife; they exchanged loving glances. "Your mother and I are too old to attempt to leave." As he patted her hand, he continued. "We will be fine here."

Then her father grabbed her hand. "Let me tell you a story I've kept to myself. On April 28, 1975, your sister, who lived in

Paris at the time . . . her husband was the hospital director here. He arranged for a plane at Tan Son Nhut to take us to Paris. Your sister and her husband feared for my life because of my role in the military. Your mother and I talked, we discussed everything. She did not want to leave but begged me to go. I could not leave her, I love her *and* I believed I would be safe. I was too old to be a concern to them, the North Vietnamese Communists." He paused for a minute to catch his breath. "I'm older now, and we have no desire to leave. Certainly, couldn't do it hopping on a boat. But I wanted you to know my background to answer your question."

Toan and Nha-Y sat speechless until Nha-Y spoke up. "Why have you never told us this story?"

He took a sip of his tea and raised the cup slightly with a shrug. "Why? It was totally irrelevant. Anyway, I will lend you the gold, what I have. You need to get out of here." He got up from the table. "Wait here."

Nha-Y frowned at Toan, who rubbed his chin with his right hand.

In less than a minute, the Judge returned carrying a bright blue bag, one hand holding the top and the other hand supporting the weight. He set it on the table.

Before her father could speak, Nha-Y looked at Toan, then at her father. "Are you sure you can afford to lend us this gold? We know it is all of your life savings."

The Judge nodded and smiled as he pushed the bag of gold toward Toan. "This is all I have, fifteen tael. Seek your dreams, Nha-Y. I want you to be free." Then he looked at Toan. "Take it and go to your meeting."

Toan looked at his wife as a tear appeared in the corner of her eye. She wiped it away with her left hand.

Toan drew a deep breath. "Do you know any place where we can come up with the balance?"

He rubbed his chin with his right hand. "Yes, there is a woman here in the complex who may help you. She owes me a favor. She has some gold. We'll go pay her a visit here in a little bit."

They sat at the table talking for a little while longer. The conversation was much lighter, less stressful. Then the Judge said, "Toan, let's go pay my friend a visit before you head back home."

The two men got up from the table and left. Nha-Y and her mother followed them to the front door.

Within an hour, Toan and his father-in-law walked back into his home and sat down in chairs across from the two women. Toan reached in his pocket and produced the eight taels of Vietnamese gold that the neighbor, Ms. Tham Man, had lent to Toan. Everything was now set; they had their fee in full to escape Vietnam.

Chapter Thirteen

Third Escape Attempt

Bien Hoa

Tuesday, February 20, 1979

After several false alarms, numerous meetings, "code-speak" phone calls, and anxious evenings, Toan received a call from Ms. Tam; she was going to stop by his private practice office the next evening. He had become almost callous to the whole situation, to the point of no longer believing she could help. Every time he took a call or had a meeting he would be let down. But being an eternal optimist, he got his hopes up each time she called; he had no other options at this point.

Ms. Tam showed up at his office. As per their normal routine, she was scheduled to be his last appointment at the end of the day. Ms. Tam sat down in front of Toan, folded her hands on his desk. "Can you be in Saigon this coming weekend?"

Toan nodded without a word.

She smiled. "Good, you will be picked up, likely by Mr. Ly, and driven to Soc Trang where you will board the boat. We will stop by your father-in-law's on Friday evening to make further arrangements."

On Thursday morning, Toan put on his concerned face and went into Director Hai Bon's office to tell him his father-in-law had fallen gravely ill. He sought permission to be off duty Friday to be with him. Hai Bon granted his request with the understanding he would be back to work on Monday, as the hospital would be short-staffed without him. Toan flashed a brief smile then went back to concern as he thanked the director and left.

After work, immediately upon arriving home, Toan asked his family to pack clothes and items for daily use for a few days. Nha-Y was ahead of him, as she had everything packed and organized plus the children were ready. They decided it was best to say nothing to their children about their escape attempt.

Quynh-Dao walked into the bedroom and joined her big sister, Quynh-Hoa, and her big brother Vu. "I guess we are not supposed to know we are going to try to escape again?"

Vu looked at her then Quynh Hoa. "They think they are so sneaky. I know they just think they are protecting us, but how obvious can it get?"

With that they all giggled.

Friday, February 23, 1979

The next morning, Toan got up and told Nha-Y they could not take their doggie Ki to their home. They did not want responsibility for an animal, but they couldn't tell the children they were trying to escape. So they agreed to put out some food and water as they had done in the past; Nha-Y set out a dish of leftover rice and a bowl of water. All the children exchanged looks then Quynh Trang and Thanh started to cry. Nha-Y told them to buck up.

All seven of them took the short walk to the train station, boarded for the quick ride to Saigon. Upon arriving in Saigon, the family split into two groups in order to fit into cycle-rickshaws, also known as *cyclocars,* to travel to Nha-Y parent's home.

That evening, while Toan and Nha-Y were still settling in there was a knock on the front door. The Judge sought out Toan to find out if he was expecting anyone. Toan frowned and said, "Maybe."

The Judge went to the door. When he opened it, he came face to face with Ms. Tam and another individual he had never met. The Judge turned and shouted, "Ms. Tam!"

Toan had not seen or heard from Mr. Phat in over a year. *It must be pay day, which was a good thing.*

They all went upstairs to Toan and Nha-Y's living area and sat down. Mr. Phat was his usual confident self. Immediately, he asked, "Dr. Vuong, your trek to freedom begins in the morning. I am here to collect my fee. I have to start to grease the wheels, if you will. So . . . it's time to get me my twenty-seven tael of gold."

Without a word, Toan got up and left the room. As he went to his bedroom, he did not hear any conversation. He figured Nha-Y was nervous and anxious. He made sure no one had followed him as he picked up the heavy blue bag, one hand on top and one underneath, holding his ransom to freedom.

Toan sat down in front of Mr. Phat and set the bag in front of him. When Mr. Phat reached for the gold, Toan put his hand on top of Mr. Phat's. "Too many unfulfilled promises," he said. "I'll bring it in the morning when your driver shows up."

Mr. Phat squinted at him for a minute, trying to intimidate him. It didn't work.

Toan stood his ground. "In . . . the . . . morning."

Mr. Phat finally nodded. "Okay, okay. Early in the morning, Mr. Ly will be here to pick up everyone. Now give me a list of all riders."

Toan went through and listed all his family members, then added his sister Minh and nephew Anh.

Mr. Phat snarled a smile at Toan as he held up two fingers. "Two members we have not discussed."

Toan nodded. "They have to bring their own payment."

Mr. Phat replied. "One tael for each of them. I want it tomorrow before Mr. Ly pulls away from the curb."

Again, Toan nodded but did not say another word. He got up, and everyone else followed Toan's lead except for Nha-Y, who remained behind. He ushered them out the door without another word.

Saigon

Just before daylight on Friday morning, Toan greeted Mr. Ly at the front door of the Cong Ly Street residence before he could knock. When Toan stepped out the door, Ly pointed at the car and its driver. As soon as his sister Minh and nephew Anh were out on the front lawn, he took them aside and they completed their business. Then he gathered everyone around him.

"He'll take you to Bac Lieu." Ly looked at Toan. "I want your gold payment."

Toan knew he was not only protecting his life savings but those of his father-in-law. He pulled out the blue bag and showed it to Ly. "When we get to Bac Lieu, I'll hand this over."

Ly snarled, "Let me see it, to make sure you have everything."

Toan handed over the bag; he shook it but did not peer inside.

"Okay, but I will not divulge the next part of the plan until Mr. Phat is paid." He handed the bag back over to Toan.

Toan took it, then walked over to Minh and Anh and took the gold tael each of them had promised and dropped them into his blue bag. He raised the bag to show Ly.

Ly turned, walked over to the driver, and they appeared to have a conversation. He pointed at Toan and the group several times. When he was finished Ly pointed them then toward the car with a smile.

Everyone moved quickly to the overstuffed car, piled in and away they went. Toan leaned over to Nha-Y and whispered, "I'm sorry you didn't get a chance to say goodbye to your parents."

With a tear in her eye, she flashed a quick smile. "Who said I didn't? I woke Mother and Father with a kiss each on the forehead before coming downstairs."

This made Toan happy. The sun was just breaking the morning sky. About the only ones on the street were proprietors opening their respective businesses. Everyone in the crowded car was happy as they passed through every single checkpoint along the way. Mr. Phat had obviously done his due diligence, acquiring all the necessary permits and greasing the wheel to smoothly pass through all checkpoints along the route to the beach community on the southern coast of Vietnam. Still, Toan's anxiety and nerves increased at each checkpoint. He was sure they would be searched, considering the gold hung from his belt inside his left pant leg. It was a long, cramped, hot drive.

When they saw Bac Lieu, everyone in the overcrowded car exchanged smiles, including the children. The driver drove down the main street for a couple of blocks and stopped in front of a small market so they could grab something to eat. Everybody piled out of the car as fast as they could and stretched out. As they slipped into the market, Nha-Y grabbed her husband's arm and pointed behind them: The car and driver that brought them were gone.

Toan quickly walked to the street and looked up and down. The car was nowhere to be seen. Toan did not know what to do or say, but he knew he had to be calm and quiet. Otherwise the group would break into an outright panic.

As everyone leaned against the stand-up counter and finished their snack, Toan knew something positive would have to break for them. He still had the gold. He was still in control. Toan walked back out to the curb and saw Mr. Ly walking in his direction. He let out his breath. Mr. Ly greeted Toan, and the two of them walked up to the others. In a low voice only those in the group could hear, he said, "Why don't you all follow me."

Everybody walked out and followed him up the street. They turned up the next block and walked to a two-story house. By the time they made it to the house, Quynh Trang and Thanh were exhausted from being cramped in the car then having to walk here. Mr. Ly led them to the attic of the house that he owned. It was very stuffy and humid in the attic, but at least they were in a good hiding place.

Early Saturday, Toan sought out Mr. Ly and handed over his twenty-nine taels of gold. He lit a cigarette. Mr. Ly sat down at a small table and counted out the gold pieces. He looked up and smiled at Toan. "Twenty-nine."

Toan just stared at the man.

Mr. Ly got up from the little table, ran his hand through his thick head of hair. "Okay, here is what Mr. Phat had planned for the day. You will get back in the same car, and the same driver as yesterday will take you to the local bus station. Be sure to get something to eat there because we don't know when you will get to eat again. From there, you will need to break into two separate groups and get into different cyclocars."

Toan asked, "From there, what?"

Ly folded his arms on his chest. "You'll be told more when you get to the next stop, the beach."

Toan was not satisfied with the answer, but assumed for the safety of the trip it was for their own good. He went and organized his family into two groups. He put himself, his wife, Quynh Dao, and Thanh in one group and Quynh Hoa, Vu,

Quynh Trang, and Anh in the other. Minh remained behind at this time. Toan watched intently for the tiny car to pull up. Once it did he hustled everybody out of the attic to the car.

Everything went okay on the drive to the bus station. They had breakfast together, including the driver. When the drivers of the two cyclocars showed up, the two groups separated and boarded. They were stopped at several checkpoints, and at each of these stops, Toan's anxiety increased. However, not once were they searched by a constable. At one stop, the second cyclocar was slowed getting away from the checkpoint, and the two cyclocars got separated from each other. This caused Toan and Nha-Y great concern for their oldest children.

After a long day, around 5:00 p.m., the cyclocar carrying Toan, Nha-Y, Quynh-Dao, Thanh, and four strangers arrived to Ho Phong. The car went across the city then u-turned and went back through the beach community.

Toan was bewildered by the driver's activity. He had the driver stop and stepped down from the cyclocar to question him. He assumed the driver was part of Mr. Phat and Mr. Ly's organization.

"Isn't this unusual? Are we leaving semi-officially or illegally?"

The driver matter-of-factly replied, "Illegally."

Toan was absolutely stunned. "I registered to leave semi-officially. I don't leave if it's illegal. Bring me back."

After half an hour wait, when no liaison person appeared, Toan gathered his family together and secured them rides back to Bac Lieu. Their ride was very stressful; once again, they were stopped at every checkpoint. This time all passengers were thoroughly searched. Toan witnessed many of the travelers' gold and US dollars seized by constables. At that particular moment, Toan felt fortunate he only had Vietnamese dong in his possession. However, he realized he had to confront Mr. Ly to get his gold back. Then he was concerned that Mr. Ly may have been stopped and had his gold confiscated.

It was dark when they finally got back to the attic of Mr. Ly's house. Toan's sister Minh was still there. Why had no one come for her? However, Toan and Nha-Y became even more anxious when they learned that the cyclocars carrying Quynh-Hoa, Vu, Quynh Trang, and nephew Anh had not returned.

Toan realized he had a real dilemma. He had to get back to work yet he had to secure his family. Despite all of this going on, Toan sought out and met with Mr. Ly. "I want my gold back, immediately."

Mr. Ly left the room for a minute, when he returned, he tossed the blue bag on the floor, it opened and a few taels spilled out. He grudgingly said, "Here you go. Twenty-seven taels." As he pointed at the bag. "You see, I had to pay one tael for permits, car rental. Plus, I had to give Ms. Tam one tael."

Toan was mad, but he understood the expenses, all but Ms. Tam getting her cut. He could deal with that later. "Look, everyone knew me and my family had done all the right things to leave semi-officially, not illegally."

Mr. Ly just looked at him without so much as a word.

Then Toan demanded, "I want a ride back to Bien Hoa. This is your misunderstanding. This is your fault. I have to try to get back to work on Monday . . . as though nothing is wrong."

Mr. Ly finally spoke. "I'll make the arrangements, but I can't do anything until morning."

That night, Toan, Nha-Y, and Toan's sister Minh sat on the attic floor and discussed their plan to return to "normal life" in Bien Hoa. They were all concerned about how it would play out. Then Toan had to make one of the most difficult decisions in his life. He looked at Nha-Y. "Will you stay here until the rest of the family arrives? I'll take Quynh-Dao back home with me in the morning. We have to make everything look as normal as possible. I told Hai Bon I would be back Monday morning. I believe that is the only chance of keeping out of trouble with the authorities. We don't want them suspicious of our escape attempts."

Nha-Y had a look of sheer terror in her eyes, but nodded. "I will gather our children and return. Make sure that Ly follows through."

Toan felt terrible about his decision, but he knew it was the right one for his family. "I promise we will get out of here one way or another."

Toan, Nha-Y, and Minh sat the rest of the evening talking about the dilemma they were in.

After midnight, Toan finally laid down to get some sleep, but it was hard to come by. He wondered where the rest of his family was. Where could they possibly be? Had they been kidnapped, or did they get on the boat? Or did the authorities grab them?

Nha-Y sat up with Toan's sister Minh talking the balance of the night, unable to sleep due to the unknown fate of their family.

Toan woke up in the middle of the night. The rest of his family had not shown up yet. He began to think about going back to work, acting like nothing was going on. Plus, he had to make up a plausible story about his father-in-law.

Chapter Fourteen

Trying to Return to Normal

Bac Lieu

Sunday, February 25, 1979

At 6:00 a.m., the designated time, a car showed up at their hideaway house. Toan and his daughter, Quynh-Dao, walked out to begin their long trek back to Bien Hoa. Toan knew he had to do everything within his powers to make everything look as normal as possible. Both took their small bags filled with their clothes. Once again, Toan hung the blue bag containing the twenty-seven taels of gold from his belt, inside his left pant leg. Since they had to go first to his in-laws then on to his home, Toan worried about the upcoming checkpoints.

At each checkpoint, the car was stopped. While his anxiety rose, they were never searched. Just after noon, as they pulled up to the My Thuan ferry, they decided to have a snack.

Toan could only play with his food, while both the driver and Quynh-Dao ate like nothing was going on. They boarded the ferry and started off for the other side.

Toan nervously looked around at some of the passengers sharing the ride. He feared he was being watched, whether by Vietnamese agents or thieves. As he glanced around, he focused on a disheveled woman who had an ugly scar on her face. She was holding a beat-up guitar. As the ferry slowly traversed the body of water, from time to time the woman would sing and play, expecting some change to be dropped in the bowl in front of her. Toan eavesdropped on a conversation between three ladies, which revealed the poor girl's sad story. She was Cam-Nhung, once a beautiful dancer, disfigured by acid tossed in her face by an order from a jealous lieutenant colonel's wife.

At about 5:00 p.m., they arrived at his in-laws' complex. Toan demanded that the driver wait while he dropped off some items before proceeding on to Bien Hoa. Toan hustled out of the car. He was met by his sister, Gai, as he ran through the front door.

She exclaimed with tears in her eyes. "Ah! Back? Your house in Bien Hoa was devastated!"

Toan stopped in his tracks with those words. He assumed she had just come from there to know this. However, he quickly re-composed himself then continued into his in-laws' home without a reply. He went straight upstairs searching for his father-in-law, to quickly tell his story. As soon as he found him, he hurriedly ripped his shirt off and unbuckled his belt.

As Toan turned back around to face his father-in-law, the Judge's head was tilted and he was frowning. Toan realized he was unaware that all his gyrations were to get to the hidden bag of gold. He drew a deep breath and reached inside his pants to produce the blue bag containing the twenty-seven taels of gold. He handed it to the man he respected so much.

But as quickly as the weird-yet-humorous moment passed, Toan's frustration and agitation returned. This caused him to struggle mightily to pull his shirt back on and buckle his pants. He had never been so clumsy. No sooner that he finished redressing than he realized he'd pulled his shirt on backwards. Both men laughed as he quickly adjusted it the correct way then headed back down the stairs. He spoke respectfully to everyone he encountered in the house, as they all had come to the stairway to see what the commotion was all about. Toan didn't stop, he just continued out the front door, toward the waiting car, which was still running.

He climbed in, forced a brief smile at Quynh-Dao, then nodded as he waved his hand for the driver to go. Toan suggested that they take the fastest, easiest route, which was the Korean freeway. As they approached that freeway, everyone noticed there was a checkpoint ahead. The driver slowed down as a constable stepped in front of the car and raised his hand straight out. He walked up to the window and asked to see the travel permit and driver's license.

The driver handed out both to the constable who pulled his flashlight and illuminated them. The constable looked at the driver one more time and said, "Your permits are good but are you aware your driver's license has expired?"

The driver looked down and replied, "No."

Then the constable asked him to open the door. No sooner was the door opened before the constable grabbed the driver, jerked him out, causing him to lose balance. Over the next few minutes, Toan watched in horror as the constable forcibly interrogated him. As the interrogation continued and became more intense, Toan saw the driver slip the constable several hundred dong; "miraculously," they were permitted to leave.

Toan looked at Quynh-Dao and smiled as he let out his breath. Fortunately, the remainder of the drive had no more such events.

A little after 9:00 p.m. they arrived at the outskirts of Bien Hoa. The driver turned toward Toan and asked for instructions to get to their residence. Toan told him to take Nga Ba Thanh and turn on Hung Dao Vuong Street. When they pulled up, both Quynh-Dao and Toan grabbed their bags and pensively walked to their home. At the front door, Toan struggled to open it and heard a voice from behind him: "Brother Toan!"

Toan spun around to be greeted by a man sprinting across the street: his brother, Trong. He was breathing hard. "Did you fail to leave?"

Toan frowned as he greeted him. "Come in, we'll talk."

Toan switched on the light and immediately jumped back as he realized water was running and the floors were soaked. His few furnishings were a mess. All the cabinet doors were open, books and medical equipment scattered everywhere. Up at the ceiling, where there was once a fan all that was left was hanging wires. Ki, their dog, came out of his hiding place barking but wagging his tail. This brought the flash of a smile to Toan's face; at least the dog was happy to see them. It had been a tough decision to leave the dog behind with only a dish of left-over rice and a bowl of water. Despair returned to Toan, and he quickly went and turned the water off downstairs.

Then Toan, Trong, and Quynh-Dao went upstairs. The staircase was soaking wet. When Toan reached the top of the steps, he turned on the lights and quickly checked each upstairs room. He entered his own bedroom and was startled to come face to face with a young Viet Cong agent.

Toan looked at the agent. "*What are you doing in my house*?"

The agent stepped toward him. "Ah! I believed you'd left!"

Toan shook his head and replied with a calmness that surprised even himself. "I didn't. I was in Saigon to visit my sick father-in-law."

The Viet Cong agent frowned, then raised his palms. "I saw kids come here to loot. . . ."

Toan walked out of the room while the Viet Cong agent was still talking and went to the rear door. It was open. Toan yelled, "Quynh-Dao, come here! Immediately!"

Back up to his bedroom, he found the door to the balcony open. He looked at the Viet Cong agent but did not speak.

The Viet Cong agent nodded. "I informed the police. They are about to come and investigate."

Toan turned back to the man. "Thank you." He half-smiled to himself as he walked out on the balcony. *I may have just pulled this off.*

Within a few minutes, Quynh-Dao walked out onto the front balcony. Toan went over to her and gave her a loving hug, then whispered, "Stay out on the front balcony."

Toan heard the door open. This time, it was Trong. The three of them sat on the balcony to make everything appear normal. Trong had his head down the whole time. Toan kept repeating over and over in a low voice, "We must stay out here and just act like nothing happened or is happening."

After sitting there for a few minutes, Trong's head was still down. "Ms. Lien, a friend of your sister Hong arrived in front of your home in a truck. They took many of your furnishings, including your ceiling fan."

Toan scowled at his brother. "Including my family's picture albums. *Seriously*?"

Trong still did not look up; all he could do was nod. "It didn't end there. When their truck got to the police checkpoint at Di An, they were stopped. The constable seized everything." He finally looked Toan in the eye.

This did not give Toan any sense of satisfaction. His home had been stripped of everything except for heavy appliances, like his refrigerator, stove, television, and one bicycle with flat tires. They even took his ceiling fan.

It was getting late, and Quynh Dao was sitting out the porch playing with a small doll she'd found in the bedroom. She was getting chilly, but her father had asked her to sit out there so all the neighbors and any authorities that drove by would see that everything was "normal."

On Monday morning, it was time for Quynh-Dao to go to school. Toan put her on their only bicycle, the one with the flat tires, and peddled her to Ngo Quyen High School. Neither Toan nor Quynh Dao had breakfast, as all their food had been stolen, too. Toan struggled as he peddled. *What will the day hold for me?* When they arrived at the school, many students were standing in front talking. When they saw Quynh-Dao getting off the bicycle, they deliberately repeated, "Dao failed to escape, there she's back!"

He elected not to pay any attention to the young people's cat-calls. He was just too exhausted. Fortunately for Toan, the hospital was a little less than a kilometer away.

As he stopped by the coffee vender outside the OB department, Toan felt bad he hadn't been able to get anything for Quynh Dao. Before Toan could even sit down to enjoy his coffee, the vender and several of the other customers looked at him and inquired, "Didn't you leave, Doc?"

All Toan could do was blow on his coffee and wryly smile. When he finished his cup, he entered the hospital as though everything was normal. Everyone greeted him with strange looks, yet no one said a word. *I knew they believed I had left. I'm sure they had all heard about my home being ravaged and furnishings stolen.* He continued making his rounds for the balance of the day, as though nothing was wrong.

Late in the afternoon, a constable came to the hospital and presented him a notice to appear at the police station the next Tuesday at 9:00 a.m. He was to meet agent Quang. Toan thanked the constable then went and sat down for a moment. Despite his attempt to escape, his day back at work had conjured some sanity to return to his life.

The next morning, after Monday's fiasco and embarrassment, Quynh-Dao rode a cyclocar to school. Her dad had told her he would bring in some groceries and she would have to prepare meals for three people including his brother Trong, who was living with them while working at the psychiatric hospital. She assumed that would be her role, at least until her mom came home. As a good student, she had a lot of homework that evening, but she knew she had no choice.

On the designated Tuesday, Toan reported to work extra early and was called to a meeting with the hospital director. *Why does the director want to see me now? If I was in trouble, wouldn't he have asked to see me the day before?* Conversely, Toan wanted to show him the police notice and seek his permission to go to the police station.

With the director's permission, Toan made his way to the police station on Cach Mang Thang Tam Street. He arrived at 8:55 a.m., five minutes before his scheduled appointment. He showed the desk sergeant his notice and was led into the next room, where he was introduced to another constable. Again, he had to show his notice.

"I'm here to meet with Agent Quang."

"Comrade Quang is on a mission," the constable replied. "Return to your work, Dr. Vuong, and we'll let you know when to appear."

Toan left the station disappointed but relieved in a strange way. He'd never been asked to appear before a constable or an agent for any reason and had no idea what to expect.

Sunday, March 4, 1979

Finally, one week after Toan returned home, Nha-Y returned with three of their children Quynh-Hoa, Quynh-Trang, and Vu. Thanh stayed with the in-laws in Saigon. Nha-Y told Toan the whole story of their plight over the last week. Vu joined them. Nha-Y started, "First, they put us in a cyclocar—me, the three kids, and Anh."

Vu spoke up, "Don't forget there were other strangers with us."

Nha-Y glanced at Vu, then continued, "We made it to Ho Phong, no problems. Then that evening they put us up in a straw-covered hut. Sometime during the night, a man we'd never seen before came and told us you all had gone back to Bac Lieu. That caught us completely off guard."

Vu spoke up again, "The man asked us what we wanted to do and Mother said, 'Go back.'"

Nha-Y picked up the story. "The man said he would get us back to Bac Lieu, but they couldn't that night."

Vu jumped in again. "Yeah, Anh stayed. He was told the boat was about to leave, and we think he went with them."

Nha-Y said, "The next morning they came and got us in a cyclocar and took us back to Bac Lieu. It took them until today to make all of the arrangements to get us home."

While she was in Bac Lieu, she composed a poem:

Bạc Liêu

Rằng đi đăng ký chẳng đi chui!
Một chuyến Bạc Liêu đủ biết đời!
Xiú mại, tầm bì ăn thoả dạ,
Vuọt biên, sinh tủ tuỏng nhu chói?
Hộ Phòng vỡ lẽ tan hỗn mộng,
Phát, Lý không tin tinh chuyện lùi.
Con lạc, hồn tan, nguòi mỉa móc,
Kìa ai áo nguợc, khéo vàng roỉ…

Nha-Y decided to return to teaching at the high school. Naturally, she heard the talk around the school about the escape attempt.

Saturday, March 17, 1979

Two weeks later

On Toan's first off-duty weekend, he decided to take his family to Saigon to visit his in-laws and sister Minh. He knew they would want to be able to see their daughter, Nha-Y, plus get the whole story of what had happened. Minh was puzzled that Anh had not returned and hoped he had successfully escaped.

Before leaving Saigon, Toan and Nha-Y left their children with their grandparents so that they could take a drive to Ms. Tam's residence. They wanted to find out about the last trip and see if Mr. Phat had planned another future trip, which he did.

Both had a lot on their minds as they drove back to their home in Bien Hoa. After getting the children off to bed, Toan told Nha-Y he wanted to talk. They talked about what they had heard from Ms. Tam. Nha-Y said matter of factly, "I want out of this mess, I want out of this country. This is not the country we grew up in."

Toan nodded in agreement. "I want out, too, but understand, the issues with escape attempts are great. We know some—or should I say, we *believe* some have made it. But for every positive story there are those who were turned back to Vietnam because the country wouldn't accept them. Naturally, the authorities were waiting for them when they got back to Vietnam. They didn't go to re-education camps, they went to prison. Then there are those that died, whether they drowned or were killed by pirates. Even the United Nations is trying to step in and improve the situation, but . . ."

His voice tailed off. He could tell before he even started quoting more statistics, Nha-Y did not care. He knew it was time to change the subject. They sat up for a few more hours planning how they wished to make one more escape attempt.

The wedding day of Nha-Y and Toan

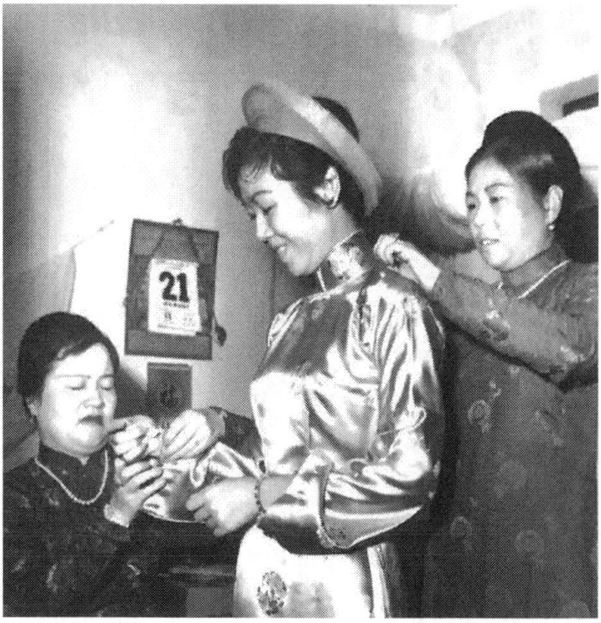

Nha-Y on her wedding day

Nha-Y and Toan's wedding party

Toan

Toan with the girls

Nha-Y and Toan with the children

Vuong family when young

Nha-Y's parents in their younger years - the Judge Pham Gia He and Nguyen Thien Bao

Nha-Y's father –
the Judge Pham Gia He

Nha-Y's mother - Nguyen Thien Bao

Nha-Y's parents, in their older years - the Judge Pham Gia He and Nguyen Thien Bao

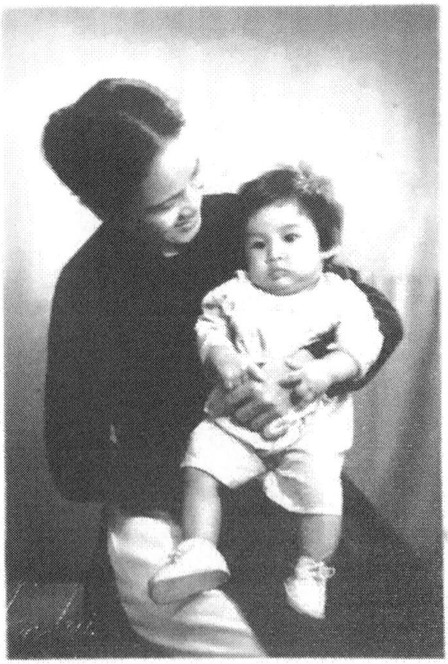

Vu with Grandmother Bao

Actual picture of the boat with the Vuong family on board

Vu at Songkhla camp

Vuong family with others at Songkhla camp

Toan and Nha-Y at Songkhla camp

Vuong family with Mr. Handojo at Galang camp

Nha-Y and her sister Hong with two other friends

A recent picture of the extended Vuong family

Vanessa's family and parents

Vu's family and parents

Dao's family and parents

Trang's family and parents

Tom's family with parents

Chapter Fifteen

Fourth Escape Attempt

Bien Hoa

Sunday, April 1, 1979

A few weeks later, when Toan again had a weekend off duty, he took his family to visit his in-laws. He had several reasons for the trip to Saigon. They wanted the children to see their grandparents as much as possible, because if they successfully escaped the next time, they would probably never see their grandparents again.

The children had been depressed ever since Vietnamese Labor Day on May 1; Toan had taken Vu and Quynh Dao to the celebration at the hospital. When they returned home, the doggie Ki was missing. He must have gotten out somehow. They looked for him everywhere but never found him. Toan believed a Vietnamese agent likely killed the dog.

Additionally, Toan was still upset with himself for a mistake he'd made months before that still haunted him. He had heard a rumor of an imminent trip, and without thinking, in a moment of excitement he'd sold his television to one of Ms. Tam's relatives. The buyer picked it up in an open cyclocar and carried it home, right down August Revolution Street. Everyone had seen it, including the authorities. He was worried this act had put him on a watch list.

They also came to Saigon to get the latest information about the next trip. Their visit with Ms. Tam confirmed that Mr. Phat had a future trip planned, likely within a few weeks. Also, while they were in Saigon, they went by to see Minh. She informed them that Anh still had not returned and hoped he had escaped.

After spending the weekend at Nha-Y's parents, they took the latest train back home. The children had gone to bed when Toan and Nha-Y decided to work on their plan to get off work and go to Saigon while raising the least suspicion possible. The plan was set and ready. They decided Toan was going to ask Dr. Hai Bon to hospitalize him at Nguyen Van Hoc, near Saigon, in order to be ready to leave on time. His need to go into the hospital was not much of a stretch, as he already had chronic gastrointestinal disease, most likely brought on by stress. Likewise, Nha-Y was going to request a week's leave from Ngo Quyen High School to go visit her ill father.

When Nha-Y was granted her request for leave, Toan went in to make the request of Dr. Hai Bon, who acted very suspicious but reluctantly granted his wish.

When Toan checked into the hospital, a young gastroenterologist who graduated from a French school, Hoang Minh Mau, was waiting for him. During the examination, Toan attempted to earn the young doctor's trust and respect, mentioning he was a classmate of other doctors at this hospital, Dr. Bach Dinh Minh and Dr. Nguyen The Minh. Toan was assigned to a ward with about thirty patients.

The next morning, Dr. Nguyen The Minh was making his rounds and visited Toan's bedside. Toan could not tell if Dr. Minh recognized him or not. In the afternoon, Dr. Mau came in to advise him they were going to transfer him to a private room.

Once Toan was in the private room, Dr. Mau returned. "I've ordered a number of lab tests, including a CT scan of your abdomen."

That evening Nha-Y came to visit. Toan could tell she was concerned. First, they were worried that the walls had ears and eyes. She leaned over to whisper in his ear. "Anh returned home. He sat in Ho Phong for a whole month waiting to board the boat, but everything fell through and he just came home."

Sadly, Toan nodded.

Nha-Y continued with more bad news, "Ms. Tam says there is an upcoming trip, but it won't be ready for a few weeks."

This made Toan worry. *Have we hooked up with the wrong people to try to escape?* He decided it was best not to say anything to Nha-Y to make her worry any more than she already was.

After about ten days in the hospital, Toan was discharged. He had no choice but to return to the hospital in Bien Hoa. All his tests had come back normal. As Dr. Mau put it, "We can't find anything wrong with you." Toan believed that the latest escape plan had either fallen through or was in hiatus. He attempted to act normal around the hospital staff, but it was difficult.

From time to time, Toan would go to Dr. Hai Bon to get a permit to go to Saigon to visit his sick father-in-law. He believed the "good director" was suspicious of his intentions: One day his beliefs were confirmed. Several State agents showed up at his father-in-law's home on a Sunday afternoon.

Fortunately for Toan and Nha-Y, they saw the agents approaching the house. Toan told Nha-Y to hustle upstairs to tell her father not to come down. When Toan let the agents in, he told them that his father-in-law had been hospitalized. They questioned him for a short time. *I know they are trying to trip me up, to say something.* When they seemed satisfied with his answers, they left.

Thursday, June 28, 1979

As Toan was finishing up his last appointment of the evening, he noticed Ms. Tam walking up to the front door. He slipped over and opened the door before she could knock.

"Dr. Vuong," she said, "are you off this weekend?"

Toan nodded as he closed the door behind her. The two of them sat down in the closest chairs and leaned toward each other as they started to talk. Ms. Tam said, "Good, good. Mr. Phat has arranged for a boat to leave Soc Trang on Saturday, so you have to make it to Saigon Friday night. Mr. Phat will arrange for a car to pick up your family early Saturday morning."

Toan asked the question he already knew that Ms. Tam could not—or would not—answer. "Do you have any further details?"

Ms. Tam got up and started toward the door. "You know how this works, Dr. Vuong. I am only giving limited information for everybody's protection."

Toan opened the door for her. "We will be ready in Saigon, Saturday morning." With that comment he closed the door and went upstairs to prepare his family.

Friday, June 29, 1979

After a wonderful meal, all the children and their grandmother left the room. The Judge got up from the table. He looked back at Toan and Nha-Y as he walked toward the door. "Wait here."

Within a few minutes, he came back carrying the blue bag with the twenty-seven Tael of gold and placed it directly in front of his daughter. With a smile he said, "Seek your dreams, Nha-Y. You know I have always wanted you to be free." He looked at Toan. "Take it and go to your meeting."

Toan picked up the bag, looked at his wife then at his father-in-law. He would go to meet with Ms. Tam and Mr. Phat, leaving behind Nha-Y to visit with her family. Toan was on a mission and was more determined than ever to get out of Vietnam.

He walked into Ms. Tam's elaborate home, and Mr. Phat was already there waiting for him. Before Toan sat down, he set his ransom for freedom in front of Mr. Phat. The man looked at the bag of gold, picked it up. He smiled as he opened it. He slowly counted each of the tael coins.

"I'll be by in the morning to pick your family up," he said when he was finished. "We will head to Soc Trang to board the boat."

Toan reached for the bag to pick it back up. Mr. Phat put his hand on top of Toan's to stop him. "This is for the organization, they want to make sure they are paid. So . . . all the proper people get paid, 'grease the wheel,' if you will. This is different from the last time."

Toan nervously nodded and left.

Saturday morning, June 30, 1979

Toan looked out the front window, waiting for the car. He could hear his family making too much noise and undoubtedly waking up the rest of the household. Toan remained on watch until 5:45 a.m., when the car pulled in front of the Judge's home. Toan walked through the house announcing that the car had arrived so as not to wake Nha-Y's parents. Within a few minutes, everyone was tippy-toeing down the stairway to the front door, carrying their small bags. Toan was surprised to see that Mr. Phat was the driver of the lead car. They all piled in.

With a big smile on his face, Mr. Phat announced in a commanding voice. “We are off to Luc Tinh.”

They were stopped at several checkpoints, but Mr. Phat had all the required permits and they were allowed to pass. Later in the afternoon, they were dropped off at a house in Soc Trang, some thirty-five kilometers to the beach. At the front door, Toan and his family were ushered to the second floor, where there were already some twenty people.

That evening Toan and his family went for a walk about the small town, as there were a few restaurants and a movie theater close. As they walked, Toan noticed another woman he recognized: Ms. Lien from Bien Hoa. She was seated at an outdoor restaurant. She made eye contact with him and nodded. She was the oldest daughter of a former sub-tenant at his office on Trinh Hoai Duc, back several years earlier. As they walked, Toan leaned toward Nha-Y and whispered, “Don’t look, there is Ms. Lien. Do you remember her?”

Before Nha-Y could answer, he continued, “If she is not trying to leave herself, within a few days everybody in Bien Hoa will know we are trying to escape Vietnam. But all we can do is continue to walk casually.”

After getting something to eat they returned to the house. The quarters were so cramped they all slept on the floor.

After a few uncomfortable days filled with delays, everyone was moved to a bigger house less than a kilometer away from the markets. The bedroom had two long beds but unfortunately, they were taken by the time Toan's family arrived. The owner of the home did provide Toan and his family blankets and a mosquito net. That evening, the owner of the house approached Toan and Nha-Y about their children. "You have little kids, it's not good for them to lie on the floor. Would you like to bring them to my son-in-law's next door?"

Toan and Nha-Y happily agreed. They took them over and saw to it that they were properly bedded down for the night. When they returned to the other house, they went out and sat on the terrace. They wanted to unwind and talked for a little more than an hour. When they were relaxed and ready for bed, they secured their valuables. Toan put his wallet under his pillow, while Nha-Y put her cash under her pillow and her purse next to her head. Exhausted, they both fell into a deep sleep.

When Toan woke up the next morning, the first thing he did was reach under the pillow for his wallet. *It was gone.* In a full blown panic, he woke Nha-Y. He had her check out her valuables immediately. Her wallet was still under her pillow.

Everything was still inside but when she went for her purse, it had been opened, all its contents spilled out. Toan went out on the terrace, looking for his wallet. As soon as he stepped out, he saw it. Excited, he snatched it up: empty. Walking to the edge of the terrace, he saw the contents of his wallet all over the ground below. Looking around, he quickly noticed a big tree sprawled over the house. That must have been how the robber got in. *Maybe the thief used some somniferous spray, likely an opiate, so nobody detected his presence.*

Toan hustled down and recovered some of the photos, but he'd lost eight hundred dong. Nha-Y lost forty US dollars she had hidden in the bra she'd taken off and placed on the mat. Luckily, she still had four hundred dong in her wallet. Both Toan and Nha-Y still had one chi of gold and a few dollars sewed inside their clothes. Despite being robbed, they elected not to tell anybody as they feared it could become an obstacle to their escape.

In spite of Toan being very low on capital or items to barter, he was able to make sure his family was able to go to the market and get meals. Every morning, Quynh Dao liked to get up early and go to the market to get her new favorite meal, banh tam bi.

While they were residing in that little village, Toan heard from several different individuals who knew him. Apparently, on the day after they left Bien Hoa, the hospital administration informed the constabulary that Toan had left, likely in order to escape. One of those same individuals went on to tell him that they had closed up his home and removed what was left of their belongings.

As the planned day approached to escape Vietnam, word was circulated that the seas were too rough for the boats. Several captains had tried to get out only to return to shore. To pacify the anxious Toan and Nha-Y, Mr. Phat picked them up, took them to the launch site to see the boat, plus gave them the name and address of its owner.

On July 1st, a rumor circulated among the "escaping community" that an international convention in Geneva, Switzerland, decided to side with the Vietnamese government. They were going to stop people from escaping the communist regime. The Vietnamese government had argued that a "brain drain" had substantially hurt their country, and surrounding countries said they could not handle the influx of immigrants.

Several days later, Mr. Phat returned with a young lieutenant constable. Mr. Phat pointed at the man with his head. "This is the man to pay, if you wish to escape."

Toan knew this was the right man. He was about thirty years old, yet he was driving a brand new Toyota pickup truck. These trucks were very pricy in Vietnam, if one could even be found. Toan decided to be blunt and ask him the key question. "Do all boats have to be 'registered' to leave Vietnam?"

With a sly smile, the lieutenant replied. "Permitted, sure! If not, everybody should be in jail!"

Despite the harshness of the lieutenant's reply, it relaxed Toan. He believed that Mr. Phat had the right connections to make their escape attempts possible.

The next day, Toan and Nha-Y went and met with the boat owner. He greeted Toan with a big smile then hustled him into the back of his boat house to show him the official list of those going on his boat. Toan picked up the list and read it carefully. He read the name of the pharmacist but was stunned neither his name, his wife's name, nor their children were listed. Toan poked his finger on the paper and looked up at the owner. "Why aren't my family's names on this list?"

The boat owner wiped his mouth with the back of his hand. "You need to go talk to Mr. Phat. That is his call."

Toan left immediately to meet Mr. Phat, thinking he had been duped yet again. It would be different this time: they could not return to their home in Bien Hoa.

Mr. Phat leaned back in his chair and raised both hands, palms up, and spoke calmly. "As you are an active doctor your name can not be officially put on the list of registration, but you will be safely escorted to board by the constabulary."

Toan realized the importance of him meeting the young lieutenant. He went back to check his funds to make sure they were ready for their escape. He had a few hundred dong, some US dollars, and ten one-chi gold rings. He hoped this would be sufficient to get out of Vietnam and to their ultimate destination, the United States of America. The good ole U.S.A.

Ten days later

Wednesday, July 11, 1979

Once again, Mr. Phat came around to tell everyone the seas were still too rough to attempt to leave. He told the gathering that for their safety, he wanted to move them to another location, where they would be less conspicuous. He had arranged cyclocars for everyone to go to the bus station downtown.

When they had all arrived, they were directed to walk down a side road to his brother Tu's house next to a canal. After walking several kilometers, they had to cross the canal. This was a long walk for Quynh Trang and Thanh. The bridge was thirty meters long and only a series of narrow boards wide, with ten bamboo poles serving as a handrail. Everyone carefully navigated the make-shift bridge. On the other side was a thatched cottage they believed to be their destination. But unfortunately, that was not the case.

They continued to walk another kilometer along the other side of the canal beside a rice field. Uncle Tu's house, another thatched cottage, was at the end of the narrow side road. It was surrounded by a rudimentary fence with a rickety gate in the front and another in the back. There were several trees and a fish pool with water supplied by the canal. In the yard, there were many banana trees and a xu dua tree close to the pond. They were told Uncle Tu raised catfish in that pond.

Once inside of the dwelling, they saw it had soil walls. It was divided into two sections furnished with long bamboo beds, and a small place used as a kitchen and a bathroom. Toan's family took one whole section with a door that opened into the back yard.

For the first week there, everyone stayed in the cottage. However, after ten days, some of the temporary residents began to go into the local village to pick up items. At first, Toan was reluctant to go or let any of his family go. Once he was sure that it was safe, every two or three days, he would take one or two of his children and walk to the market to purchase food for his wife to cook. He picked up coffee and cigarettes for himself.

One afternoon, Toan was looking for the Chinese sausages he had stowed away for himself and his family, but they were not to be found. All he could conclude was that Uncle Tu's dogs found them.

As the days passed, Toan's frustration grew. He went to Uncle Tu. "I wish to speak to Mr. Phat?"

Uncle Tu replied, "He not back from Saigon yet."

To add to his discomfort with the settings, Nha-Y believed her cooking was imposing on Aunt Tu, so she asked Aunt Tu to prepare meals. To their frustration, she charged Toan thirty-five dong per day for the modest meals.

Toan's money was rapidly dwindling. Moreover, the impact of the international decision to side with the Vietnamese government regarding escapes had caused the value of gold to slip locally. This was hurting Toan's bargaining powers. His most recent sale of one chi of gold brought him only one hundred-eighty dong or five days of meals. This was not a good situation, and no end was in sight.

Remembering these hiding days of Toan's family, Nha-Y composed the poem:

Sóc Trăng

Vùa mới Bạc Liêu lại Sóc Trăng,
Vì ham đi quá hoá tin sằng!
Hứa liểu, đón bậy, tàn có nghiệp,
Đăng ký, canh me, độc dối gian.
Chờ bão vùa xong, chờ cấm lệnh,
Cuóp ngày chua thỏa, cuóp đêm tràn!
Một nhà bảy miệng còn tay trắng,
Bốn biển không đường ... lệ chừa chan.

Chapter Sixteen

A Cottage in the Middle of Nowhere

Saturday, August 11, 1979

The Vuong family had lived in the thatched cottage for more than a month. It was obvious to Toan that the children had adapted much better than the parents. Each of the children made poles from bamboo branches to fish in the canal. They had fun despite being unsuccessful at catching anything most days. But one day Quynh Dao caught a big shrimp. Aunt Tu was more than happy to throw it in a pot to make soup. By this time, Toan was making frequent trips into the village to pick up a few items, including his cigarettes.

One trip was very memorable. It had been raining quite a lot; the road was very slippery and overflowing with mud. Toan's sandals became slick. After Vu had crossed the plank wooden bridge, Toan followed but almost fell into the canal.

When he got to the other side, he had to sit down to keep his heart from "pounding out of his chest" because he could not swim.

Then there was another not-so-good day for the Vuong family. Aunt Tu handed Nha-Y some old, ratty clothes, told her to go to the market in the village and try to sell them. She wanted a commission for any sales. Nha-Y believed that the clothes were too old to be sold, but she took them anyway. Vu helped her carry the clothes to the village. After they sat there most of the day without any takers, Nha-Y began to get nervous that she would be recognized. Finally, around 5:00 p.m., as her fear peaked, as well as her frustration, they returned to the thatched cottage. Aunt Tu was very upset and implied they had not tried hard enough to sell the old clothes.

After a few more days, Toan and Nha-Y became more and more concerned about their failing plight. It seemed they had stumbled into another lost cause to escape the communist regime of Vietnam yet there was no turning back. They could not return to their jobs. They could not go home. To pass the time in the evenings, Toan would sit on the bed and tell his children stories about what life was going to be like once they got to the United States. He told them about getting cookies, candies, sodas from vending machines—they were captivated.

However, Nha-Y was having a difficult time handling the entire situation. She seemed to be sad all the time.

Uncle Tu took note of Toan's family situation and recommended that Toan go and sell chu CS lottery gambling tickets. He had been lucky in the past; his winnings had allowed him to supplement his income each week in the past. Aunt Tu tried to cheer up Nha-Y when Toan would return with his weekly winnings, but it was not working.

Being away did not prevent Toan and his family from seeing his brothers, sisters, and in-laws; they all took turns coming to visit. However, as the situation deteriorated due to more delays and a never-ending series of stories, Toan asked his brother-in-law to take Vu, Quynh Dao, and Quynh Trang to sister Chinh's home in Vĩnh Long. When Toan saw that that was a good thing for his children, but it only made Nha-Y more sad, almost depressed. So Toan asked his brother-in-law to take Nha-Y and Thanh, as well. In the end, only Toan and Quynh Hoa stayed at Uncle Tu's family cottage. Since it was just the two of them, Toan asked Aunt Tu to get rice and food at the market and Quynh Hoa took over the cooking, housekeeping, and the laundry.

Toan continued to play Chu CS and continued to win enough money to keep his family in the necessities of life and him with his cigarettes, too. However, one night, Toan lost one hundred dong. He was devastated.

Nha-Y later composed the poem 'Thủy Tận Sơn Cùng' in memory of their hiding days in the fields after the failure of our escape attempt:

Thủy tận sơn cùng, ruộng Sóc Trăng,
Cầu tre heo hút, cỏ lan đồng...
Nhà tranh một mái che trói tạm,
Kinh rạch đôi bờ khóc mộng chung.
Vuợt biển long đong đành mất nghiệp,
Lánh thân cùng quẫn phài cam lòng!
Huyện đề một thủa ai nguời cũ.
Trứng hẹ, canh ngò "có lý" không?

With the passing of another month, Toan realized he was running out of money, fast. The reality set in that the escape was not to be this time. When Hoang came to visit, Toan and Quynh Hoa decided it was time for them to leave with him. So they went to the village and boarded a bus to Vinh Long to go stay with his sister. By this time, Nha-Y and the children had gone to her parent's home in Saigon.

Toan spent the next few days contemplating his next move. They had to escape Vietnam. They had lost everything: their jobs, their belongings, their home. All they had was literally the clothes on their backs and what few gold rings and US dollars they had to escape. On top of that if they were caught they would surely be arrested. While the authorities did not go out and seek to arrest individuals, the Vuongs would have to either bribe their way out of the predicament or face the consequences. Since Toan was short on funds, he could not pay anybody off. He elected to stay for a short time in Vinh Long, just to be by himself to think.

While he was in that part of the country, he went to Can Tho to visit his brother Thai, who took him to Ninh Kisu dock. There, Toan had the best dinner he had had in the longest time. They spent the night in Can Tho, then returned to Vinh Long the next day. By the time he returned, he decided his best move was to rejoin his family at his in-laws' home in Saigon. Now not only was Toan and his family's situation grave and dangerous, but now their presence at his in-laws' home was putting them in peril, too. His brothers, Huong, Trong, and Cat had already escaped, or so he believed. However, they had not heard anything from them since they'd left.

Shortly after Toan returned to Saigon, Nha-Y and Toan sat down late one evening and talked. During the course of their conversation regarding how they must put together another attempt to escape the communists, Nha-Y grabbed Toan's hand. "Honey, you must go and talk to Mr. Phat and get back our gold, my father's gold."

Toan knew she was right. So he agreed that first thing the next day he would go to Ms. Tam's residents and get their gold. It was Mr. Phat who had failed to perform.

The next day, Toan borrowed a moped, so that he and Nha-Y could go to Ms. Tam's home. They wanted her to accompany them to go meet Mr. Phat. She agreed to go, but Mr. Phat failed to appear for the appointment. This was just the first of many trips to Ms. Tam's then on to Mr. Phat's for a scheduled appointment. Each time, Mr. Phat failed to show; naturally, he always made an excuse for missing those appointments.

Over the next several months, Toan and his family had no alternative but to stay with Nha-Y's parents. Naturally, from time to time, a constable came around looking for them. Fortunately, they were always tipped off, usually by one of the judge's friends, Mr. Thanh, who was kind of the "neighborhood mayor."

However, the delicate situation put everyone on edge, especially Nha-Y's father, the former judge. One evening after dinner it was just the Judge, his wife, Toan, and Nha-Y sitting at the kitchen table drinking coffee. The Judge looked at his daughter, then his son-in-law. "I have never worried about what the communists would do to me. I always believed I was too old to be a concern. But I must tell you both that if Thanh or anybody else in the neighborhood does not see the authorities coming and they come busting through the door, everybody in this house could end up in hard labor camps until we die."

Toan had worried about his in-laws but hearing the Judge come right out and say it was startling. Nha-Y's mother, Bao, spoke up. "Why don't you all go register with the government and get put on the official list to leave the country?"

Nha-Y grabbed Toan's arm under the table. "Mother, that is the worst thing we could do. We wouldn't even be allowed to leave the building." She glanced at her father. "They would do just as Father said—we would be sent to a hard labor camp. Our children would be stuck in Vietnam for the rest of their lives."

From the look on Bao's face, Toan believed she had not thought through the ramifications if everything went wrong. Toan loved his in-laws very much and realized the horrible predicament he and his family had put them in. His mother-in-law, despite Toan's inability to contribute living expenses, had somehow managed to keep both families fed.

Bao smiled a sad smile at Nha-Y. "I am sorry. That was wrong of me to say. I am just worried about your father."

Toan tried to calm everyone down. "I will try harder to get a way to escape so as not to put you all at risk any longer. We have put you all in a very bad situation."

To recall the stay at her parents', Nha-Y wrote the poem:

Công Lý

Trốn mãi, ặn hoài cũng trắng tay,
Liều về Công Lý sống qua ngày.
Cơm cha áo mẹ thêm lần nũa.
Ẩn nhẫn chờ thời họa có may!
Vàng đã trao ra đòi chẳng đuợc,
Nguòi mong đi khuất lại về đây!
Một nhà ở lậu, ăn tiêu ké,
Tóc bạc vì con lệ đã đầy...

Chapter Seventeen

Trying to Get My Gold Back

Saigon

Monday, December 17, 1979

The Vuongs knocked on the door of Ms. Tam's residence. They had lost track of how many times they'd come to see her. Ms. Tam greeted them at the door. Toan and Nha-Y followed her to her elaborate living room. Toan had hoped to see Mr. Phat waiting on them, but once again was disappointed that he was a no-show. When they all were seated, Ms. Tam leaned forward and smiled. "I have great news."

Toan had heard her say that so many times, those words had become meaningless.

Ms. Tam continued, "Mr. Phat has agreed to give you back your fifteen taels of gold. He was not able to get the twelve taels he used to bribe the lieutenant constable."

Toan let out a deep sigh, but he was not surprised; a man with a new Toyota pickup did not get one by returning bribes.

Ms. Tam responded to his sigh. "I am not done, Dr. Vuong. I am doing all I can to find another trip organizer. Please be patient with me and just allow me a little more time. I will come through for you."

Toan exchanged a quick glance with Nha-Y, who flashed a half-hearted smile.

Thursday, January 3, 1980

Ms. Tam kept the promise she had made to the Vuongs. Several weeks earlier, she had stopped by the Pham Gia He residence to pick them up to go meet an ethnic Chinese man, Mr. Luong, who was willing to assist them with their escape. When they arrived, Mr. Luong told them he had a cargo ship of iron; he even showed them a picture of the ship. Plus, he promised to make Toan a manager, so that his family could stay in his cabin.

A few days later, Toan went back over to see the ship's captain. He told Toan to get Chinese names for all his family. Over the next couple of weeks, Toan apparently developed a good relationship with Captain Luong; the man seemed on top of matters and had good updates. Toan was very optimistic that he had finally found the man, which was good. The situation in Vietnam was getting progressively worse. The Communist Party had begun to implement land reform and collectivism for sharing farm production. He knew this was an additional recipe for failure. There was already little food, and the details of the program foreshadowed even less.

Thursday, January 17, 1980

Late in the evening, Ms. Tam came by the He residence to tell Toan that Mr. Luong's ship would be leaving Saturday morning. The next afternoon, Friday, they needed to have their bags packed and food bagged—no more than ten bags in total—and take it all to Mr. Luong's home to be loaded. This way they would not be so obvious walking around. They were to be in front of the National Academy of Music, Saturday morning, where a car would pick them up and take them to a ship anchored in a Saigon river dock.

Early Saturday morning, Toan and his family were anxiously standing in front of the National Academy of Music. They were too exposed, out in the open, so to keep from being too obvious, they walked up and down the street for the next five minutes or so. A stranger approached them and pulled Toan aside. "Are you supposed to be going on Captain Luong's ship?"

Toan did not know what to say. He just stared at the man.

The stranger looked both ways; it was obvious he was anxious, too. "The authorities are watching that ship. Someone tipped them off." With that, the man turned and almost sprinted away from Toan.

They had no choice but to return to their in-laws' home. The next day, Toan and Nha-Y went to Mr. Luong's home. They knocked and knocked, but no one answered. Then they went to Ms. Tam's. When the door opened, it was not Ms. Tam but one of her relatives, who said, "Ms. Tam left yesterday morning for Bien Hoa."

Toan asked, "When will she be back?"

The woman just closed the door in Toan's face. Toan and Nha-Y was stunned by her rudeness. Once again, Toan and his family had failed to escape. Once again, they had lost all their belongings, which were now very few.

A poem was composed by Nha-Y with the title:

Lẻng Sung

Tàu sắt đâu rồi ới Lẻng Sung?
Tuỏng rằng mạt lộ gặp anh hùng!
Vuợt biên năm phút đồ vơ sạch,
Húa hẹn trăm lần chuyện vẫn không!
Quản lý để râu chờ đỏ mắt,
Lẻng Sung cuốn gói lẩn nhu trùng.
Trơ trơ tàu sắt nằm trên giấy,
Mất cả quần ngoài lẫn áo trong!

Wednesday, January 23, 1980

Toan and Nha-Y went to see his brother Kien in Ban Cơ. It was approaching the time of the year to honor the dead, and Toan and Kien wished to honor their parents during the approaching Tet. They had done so in the past, but everybody's finances were so poor this year, it would not be possible. Instead, they decided all the brothers would just go to the parents' grave site.

Little time was spent discussing their ceremony. Most of it dealt with the many failed escape attempts and the perils of their failures. Kien had also tried to escape and was unsuccessful. They discussed teaming up. Kien informed Toan that they had a cousin, Vu Thin, who lived in the United States. He also said another family member had made it to Australia. While the two brothers talked, Nha-Y just refused to participate. Toan knew his talking about all their failures only depressed her. This did not keep Toan from speaking about his determination to find a trustworthy organizer.

When the men finished talking, they went to pick up Can then to their parents' tomb in Go Vap. On the drive back, the conversation turned back to desires to escape. Can wondered out loud if the unrest in Thailand, which had led to the resignation of Prime Minister Kriangsak, could place an additional hurdle to future attempts. Toan told his brothers, "It is obviously too early to tell. I believe because of the influence of the United States, Thailand will try to continue toward some form of democratic rule."

Toan and Nha-Y delayed going back to her parents' as long as possible. Their presence continued to add to the strife at the residence, which was made even tenser by her sisters Hong, Oanh, and Phuong, who were also living there.

When Tet arrived, it was the saddest holiday either of them could remember. Not only because of their own failures to escape but because staying at Nha-Y's parents' home was becoming a huge imposition. Moreover, Toan had not heard any word of Huong, Trong, or Cat; all of them had likely escaped several months ago but there had been no word from them. They did not know if they had made it to freedom or if they had been captured or died.

Despite the high risk, in an attempt to assist his in-laws, Toan decided to do some medical practice on the side to make a little money for his family. While it was far below their previous living standard, it was better than more than ninety percent of the citizens. Plus, it allowed him to handle some of his guilt hiding out at his in-laws' home, as he was able to provide for all those living under the single roof. Every time someone escaped, Nha-Y upped the pressure on Toan to find a way, *any* way, to escape. But Toan had only four hundred U.S. dollars and six taels of gold, which he had had a jeweler mold into crude rings.

Chapter Eighteen

And So It Begins Again

Saigon

4:00 a.m., Wednesday, March 26, 1980

The alarm startled him awake. He sat straight up in bed. Had he been dreaming? Had he not slept? *Will our fifth escape attempt be successful?* Ms. Tam sure didn't need to pound on the door like she had the night before. *She was either trying to frighten us or just being dramatic. Probably both.*

All the family members who planned to escape gathered in the Pham Gia He's living room. Toan had spent some time figuring out how to divide them into three groups before they went out to meet the motored cabs.

"Everybody wearing the clothing with the valuables sewed up in the hems?" he asked. He glanced around. The adults were nodding the children were fingering their hems. He took that as a positive response.

He drew a deep breath and told Nha-Y, "You take Vu and Thanh with you. Okay, that's one group." Then he looked at Hong, Nha-Y's youngest sister. "You take Ms. Lien and Quynh Dao with you." He turned back to Quynh Hoa and Quynh Trang. "Both of you will come with me."

Toan was unsure of his plan for dividing his family. He and Nha-Y had quickly decided that he would take Quynh Hoa and Vu would take her, to attempt to prevent his oldest daughter and his wife from being raped should they be confronted with men with those intents.

Then Toan tried to lighten the mood of the travelers by making a dad statement. "Everybody should try to go to the bathroom before we leave. Who knows when we will see toilets again?"

This brought a few laughs, but he was serious: His chronic gastrointestinal issues had flared up again. As it was his turn to go into the room, he was having serious cramps, likely brought on by the stress of the moment. *How could all my tests come back negative? That gastroenterologist doesn't know what he was doing or the tests were messed up.*

As everyone shuffled into their respective groups, he made one more statement. "We will likely get separated once we get into the cabs. We are instructed if we run into one another, we are to act like we don't know each other. Everybody got that?"

There was some giggling among the children, but from the looks on the adults' faces, he believed they grasped the seriousness of this escape process. Their lives could depend on what they did or didn't do. With that, Toan started walking, and all the groups dropped in line behind him.

When everyone was outside, the stillness of the early morning was highlighted by the few streetlights as they all walked to the curb and slowly separated into their groups of three. Toan noticed how everybody looked not at the individuals in their respective groups but at those in the other groups. The first cab pulled up. Nha-Y's group got in and off they went into the night. Within a few minutes, the second cab stopped in front of the house and Quynh Dao's group climbed in. The cab to pick up Toan's group pulled up in another ten minutes. As soon as they pulled away from the curb, Toan asked the driver, "Where are we headed?"

The driver leaned back. "I have instructions to take you to the bus station at Luc Tinh."

Toan looked at him intently. "I thought we were going to Rach Gia."

The driver shook his head. "That's all I know. Bus station at Luc Tinh."

Toan glanced around at the hushed, sleeping neighborhood as the cab passed under each streetlight, capturing the images of a city he hoped he would never see again. It took about a half an hour to make it to the bus station at Luc Tinh. As the cab was coming to a halt, he and his group prepared to step down.

The cab disappeared into the night as Toan looked around for a brief moment; a stranger approached them and handed them tickets. He whispered to Toan. "Follow me." The stranger was the next guide and pointed with his head. "Your group will follow me up the sidewalk toward the bus departing for Rach Gia."

Toan and the two young people did as requested. As they walked, he stepped alongside Toan and spoke in a low voice. "When we have boarded the bus, somewhere along the trip, I'll pull on my ear. That means we have to get off the bus, no matter what, when, or where. Got it?"

Toan frowned. While he understood the gesture, he didn't understand what the man was trying to tell him. Nonetheless, he nodded. *What? When? Or where?*

After walking about ten minutes, the three of them arrived at a bus boarding for Rach Gia. As Toan walked toward the bus, it pulled away from the station. He let out a sigh, thinking he had failed once again. But to his relief, ahead the bus stopped to pick up more passengers. The guide was able to get the bus to remain in its place until Toan and his group could board. It seemed like the bus stopped every ten to twenty meters to allow more to board.

Several blocks up, Toan saw Nha-Y, Vu, and Thanh step onto the bus. Toan and his group stayed to themselves so they could feign ignorance of the others from his family. It was difficult ignoring his wife in such anxious moments. His anxiety peaked when he realized he still had not seen Quynh Dao's group.

As the bus traveled away from Luc Tinh ever so slowly, it came upon various checkpoints. At each point, the driver was asked to step down by the constable. Toan looked down each time so he did not have to watch the interaction in case things went wrong. But before the constable was done—each time—he looked up anxiously. Each time, the driver would hand the constable an envelope. Each time, each stop, Toan held his breath; if the bus was searched both he and his wife would be going to re-education camps. *Who knows what would happen to his children?*

These stops were extremely stressful. He was certain the envelopes contained money, likely US dollars. Each time, the bus was permitted to pass. Like any normal bus, it stopped often to either pick up or drop off more passengers. With each stop, Toan looked around to see if they had been boarded by Vietnamese agents; it would be obvious if they were.

About an hour into the trip, it stopped for ten minutes to permit passengers to go to the toilet. This was a great relief to Toan. Every time the bus arrived in a town, the bus stopped and child venders brought baskets of cookies, candies, fruit, and drinks to offer passengers. *Still no sign of Quynh Dao's group.*

Finally, after a few more stops, they reached the Mi Thuaen ferry. Everyone stepped off the bus and it drove on, the passengers boarding the ferry without incident. As soon as they were safely on, the bus also drove onto the boat.

As soon as the ferry reached the other side, the driver pulled the bus off and everyone reboarded.

A little before 5:00 p.m., the bus pulled off the road in the middle of nowhere, about five to six kilometers from their destination. Their guide gave a discreet signal for both groups of their family to get off now. Once again, each group was put in separate Lam cabs and went off in different directions with Rach Gia the destination—or so he hoped. *Still no sign of Quynh Dao's group.* Toan agonized over the whereabouts of his daughter. He assumed Nha-Y was doing the same. After a half hour ride, they were at the edge of Rach Gia. Toan was relieved. They had made it to the coastal city. They proceeded to the cab station where their handler said, "Stop right here and wait. Another handler will pick you up here. My part of the assignment is finished."

When Toan tried to ask about the rest of his family, the handler put his finger up to his mouth. He turned and walked away quickly.

Toan and his two children stood there for a couple of minutes. Another man walked up to Toan: "Dr. Vuong, you are to follow me."

Toan and his children picked up their small bags and followed the handler. After walking a little ways, Toan asked him, "Why have we not seen the other members of our group?"

The handler replied, "Each group is deliberately taking different city streets to the waiting boats. That way our operation doesn't look obvious."

As Toan and his family carried their bags through the city streets, he got very nervous. Other people on the streets were giving him strange looks. He became more and more paranoid that he would be recognized. He expected to be grabbed by Vietnamese agents at any minute. Yet, no one approached them, including several constables they passed as they walked.

Hong, Ms. Lien, and Quynh Dao were told "wait here," so they found a bench to sit on until the handler returned. He'd said he would be back within a half hour. They cling to the small bags of their possessions, waiting. The handler was two hours overdue when Ms. Lien gave Hong a worried look. More time passed. When Ms. Lien was sure Quynh Dao was not paying attention to the two adults, she leaned over and whispered, "I'm afraid the handler has skipped out on us. I think we better start to figure out how to get back home."

Hong bit her lower lip as she tried not to show her stress. "Do you think he got on the boat and left without us? Or do you think he got caught? What if the constables show up?"

Ms. Lien patted her longtime friend's hand, sitting back and looking straight forward. She didn't seem to be focused on anything.

After several more minutes, a worried and heartbroken Hong leaned forward and looked up and down the street. It was eerily quiet. This was her best chance to escape. At this point, they needed to get home without getting arrested. Hong started to pull a corner of her blouse where she had sewed Vietnamese dong, "So we should take some of our money to pay our way home?"

Ms. Lien looked at both Quynh Dao and Hong, "Yes, it's are only choice. Let's try to make it to your father's house."

The two women stood from the bench. Hong looked at Quynh Dao. "Let's go."

Quynh Dao titled her head as she looked up at the two women.

Just then around the street corner came the cyclocar with the handler waving his hand. The rickshaw stopped, and Ms. Lien got in the handler's face. "Where have you been?"

The Handler shrugged. "The boat is full. We had to figure out a way to make room for you." He pointed at them.

They climbed in the cyclocar, and it pulled away.

As darkness set in, the handler walked them to an isolated house that sat back from the street, surrounded by large trees and shrubs. They were asked to hand over their baggage; it would be sent ahead to the boat. Toan did not want to bring attention to his stamp collection, but he had grave concerns it would get lost in the process. He went to the handler and carefully crafted his question.

"May I keep that one small package and my cartoon of cigarettes with me?"

The handler looked down at the package, then back up at Toan. "No, everything must go ahead. This will avoid your items possibly being confiscated by the constabulary. If you can secure your cigarettes, they're okay."

Toan nodded as he turned and secured the carton before walking over to set down his most valued collection.

At this time, only six of Toan's family had arrived at the secluded house. The handler returned and asked them to follow him. They moved from one house to another along very dark, muddy, uneven, narrow roads and paths. They held hands to stay together while attempting to keep up with their handler. Toan lost track of time. His children tired yet they continued to walk at the same pace.

Finally, around 10:00 p.m., they entered a poorly lit house. They sat down and rested, attempting to get comfortable. Between ten and fifteen minutes later, the handler returned again and ordered everyone out behind the house. It was very dark. They were asked to hide either in the pigpen, the toilet, or the back yard. Toan and Nha-Y looked at each other in unadulterated fear. In what little light there was, the hiding places looked small, dark, and menacing. Had they been led to their deaths?

Another hour passed. The handler returned and took two of them at a time. When it was Toan's turn to go, he took Quynh Hoa with him. They crossed a small road to enter yet another house. He held Quynh Hoa's hand as they entered. Again, their stay was brief. Soon, all of them were ordered to go to the back yard and followed a canal to where a few sampans were tied in a line. Toan helped his daughter aboard. The sampans were so small that when each member of the family stepped into the boats, they rocked so violently Toan believed they would capsize and drown them.

Time was moving very slowly while they sat in those rocking boats tied to the dock. The handler returned and ordered everyone out of the sampans. Toan held Quynh Hoa's hand to pull her ashore. Once everyone was out of the sampans, all Toan's family ran across a small courtyard to enter another secluded house. They were quickly hustled into an unlit room. Toan could hear whispers, but it was so dark, he could not tell how many people were in the room.

From time to time, a voice was heard. "Shut up! The constables are coming!"

After awhile Toan was able to whisper and find six members of his family. Still no sign of the group of three with Nha-Y's youngest sister, Hong, Ms. Lien, and Quynh Dao.

Just before midnight, Toan noticed a light coming from the adjacent room. He went to check it out. Someone had put a kerosene lamp in there and lit it. Despite the dim light, Toan could see the people in the crowded room and immediately began searching for Nha-Y and his children. Spotting them on the far side of the room, he pushed his way over to them through the crowded room.

No sooner did he reach his wife to give her a big hug and kiss than a handler stepped into the room and ordered everyone to move to the boat in groups of two at a time. *Noah's Ark . . . where are the giraffes*? Toan nodded at Nha-Y and grabbed Quynh Trang's hand and held it. As Toan slowly started to walk across the paved back yard, lit by a single distant bulb on the top of a pole, he moved slowly to keep

Quynh Trang close by. However, Toan's long-sleeved white shirt stood out so brightly that someone in the house behind them shouted, "Hurry up! Wearing white to leave—it'll alert the constables!"

Quynh Trang heard the voice and hurried to keep up. Father and daughter entered the bottom of the boat to a space of some cubic meters in the stern. Already in the tight area were a woman and two children. The kids were shrieking, their mother cursing. The place was so tight no one could not move or extend their limbs. After a short time, Toan's body went numb. But not his mind. It was firing so many questions. Where was the big boat they were promised? Was he going to be stuck in this little area the whole trip? Had Nha-Y and his three other children Quynh Hoa, Vu, and Thanh, made it on the boat? At this point, he had no way of knowing. Most important, where was Quynh Dao?

For several hours, the passengers remained crammed into place on this tiny sampan. Toan felt as though he was suffocating, but he could raise his head up to draw a breath of fresh air. From time to time, he would put his fingers under Quynh Trang's tiny nose to make sure she was still breathing. The situation was becoming more stressful, tense, and dangerous. Eventually, they pulled away from the shore.

Reading the morning sky, Toan could tell it was just after daybreak. Toan looked through the hatch board covered by a fishing net. With a great push against the board, he could spot Vu close by, on the deck of the tiny sampan. Toan nodded. "Are you all right, son?"

Vu had been among the very select few to remain on top of the tiny sampan because he was attired to look like a fisherman. It was a glorious, gorgeous day, the sun climbing into the cloudless sky. While Vu was hungry, he was enjoying most of the experience. The big drawback was that he was seated on some boards that were slimy from fish being dragged across them. He was happy and relieved to see a tiny peek of his father's face and hear his voice. Vu leaned down. "The boat is well out to sea."

He wanted to tell his father what was going on. "I was told by the handler that me and a couple of other young men had to stay on the deck and act like fisherman."

He could tell from his father's face this pleased him and he likely understood the reasons. He saw his father pushed hard against the board, but it still would not move.

Toan asked, "Can you reach this board and pull it up?"

Vu turned around, but the space between the seat and the board was very restricted. Still, he was able to pull the board up because of the limited leverage and the added weight and restriction of the fishing net. The board moved slightly, and a beam of sunlight struck his father's face, causing him to shut his eyes tight. Toan squirmed around on his back in the limited space to see up through the hatch. He saw the undulating waves and experienced a momentary feeling of happiness.

Within a few seconds, Vu could tell he had provided his father great relief, he could see the sunlight and he saw his father's chest heave, breathing in some fresh, open air.

This feeling of happiness didn't last long. Toan went into head-of-the-family mode. "Vu, can you see your mother, brother, and sister?"

Vu looked back down at his father and smiled. "No, but Mother, Thanh, and Quynh Hoa are up on the bow of the boat."

This allowed Toan to relax again. They sailed quietly for several hours.

But things weren't so good for Vu. After sitting on the deck the remainder of the day, the sun beating down on Vu made him so hot he got very ill.

Chapter Nineteen

The Big Boat

At sea somewhere in the Gulf of Thailand

9:00 a.m., Wednesday, March 26, 1980

Toan was feeling mentally relaxed despite still being crunched into the small space below deck. They were away from Vietnam's shore, and he was thinking his journey to freedom had begun. Despite it being very hot and humid, he drifted off to sleep. . . only to be awakened by whispering from above, on the deck.

"About to arrive," he heard. Within a few minutes, there was even a louder rumble as the man in charge of the sampan gave the order to transfer to the other boat. Toan and Quynh Trang were still barely able to move. Within a few minutes, Toan was jostled by a collision and felt the sampan pitch and roll.

Toan could hear shuffling above him; he assumed passengers were being transferred to a larger boat. As the passengers above moved out, people down below were freed from their very cramped quarters, including Toan and Quynh Trang. All this activity increased the rocking of the sampan. Finally, they were able to go up on the deck. The Big Boat was not nearly as roomy and didn't look as capable as he had expected. Toan wondered if it would be able to negotiate the seas of the Gulf of Thailand.

Just as he was about to step over onto the Big Boat, it began to roll and pitch from wave action. For a brief moment, he felt as though he might fall in and drown. A stranger reached out his hand from the boat and steadied Toan to step aboard. Toan turned to help Quynh Trang switch boats. With Quynh Trang aboard, Toan turned to find Nha-Y, Quynh Hoa, Vu, and Thanh. By the time he pushed his way over to his wife, all the children except for Quynh Dao had gathered. Toan hugged Nha-Y and all his children. He and his wife turned their attention to Quynh Dao. *Where was she?*

Toan surveyed how small the Big Boat turned out to be, nothing more than a taxi boat. She was no more then ten meters long and two meters wide, designed to only run inside a bay or harbor, not on the open seas. A crewman came up and ushered Nha-Y, Quynh Trang, and Thanh to the cabin.

The same crewman returned momentarily. "Dr. Vuong, do you want to get word back to your family in Vietnam?"

Toan grabbed the paper and quickly scribbled a few sentences to his in-laws that they were safely on board the Big Boat. He signed the paper and handed it back to the crewman.

Just then he heard a commotion from the other side of the boat. Toan peeked around to see another sampan approaching. It held his daughter Quynh Dao, his sister-in-law Hong, and her friend Ms. Lien. Toan shouted down to Nha-Y, "Quynh Dao is arriving."

Toan was relieved. All his family had made it to the boat, along with the others traveling in the group. No sooner had they boarded when sister Hong's face turned green and she began vomiting. Hong and Ms. Lien were ushered to the cabin.

A crewman brought around three of their travel bags. The Big Boat, which was made for just eighteen people, had a total of fifty-four passengers. Toan moved through the crowd to check the bags. His stamp collection was not in them. He had begun to accumulate those stamps back during his days attending Albert Sarraut High School in 1942. He inquired about the other bags he was hoping would show up. The crewman advised that the rest were coming. He remained hopeful he would see his stamps again.

Another crewman came around and started assigning places for everyone to occupy; Toan, Quynh Hoa, Quynh Dao, and Vu were packed in a fish compartment. All four of them occupied a space two meters wide. They had to sit leaning their backs on one side with one leg flexed, as the other side was occupied by another member.

Once Toan settled into the fish compartment as best they could, the boat engine hummed and vibrated throughout as it slid along the water. Next stop, Thailand.

Their boat sailed in a southwesterly direction while a fatigued but relaxed Toan fell asleep. He had not been able to get any rest for several nights due to the stress of attempting to watch over his family.

Toan was startled awake by voices surrounding him, both inside the fish compartment and outside. He did not feel the vibration of the boat engines as before. That was when he realized what all the whispering was about . . . engine failure. Toan raised his wrist to look at his watch. He had not slept very long, and it was likely that the boat had only traveled a few kilometers. Toan slipped out of the fish compartment to assess the situation.

He let out a heavy sigh. He could still see the few scattered houses on Vietnamese shore, not more than a few kilometers away. The Vietnamese Navy could still come at any second and take them back to shore to send them to a hard labor camp. His frustrations returned. He crawled back into the fish compartment to join his family. No sooner had he squirmed and wiggled back into place when he heard a woman's voice outside.

"Most likely the sailors are manipulating us. They want a few chỉs of gold as bribery from each family to restart the engine." A knock came from the outer hatch door, and the same voice was directed toward Toan: "Dr. Vuong, you were chosen to be our spokesman. You should go negotiate."

Another voice continued: "See the owner of the boat!"

Toan pushed the door open again and crawled back out underneath the legs of another passenger. "What is the captain's name?"

One of the two women raised her hands palms up, then pointed. "Don't know, but that's him. He's the man with a mustache."

Toan looked in the direction the woman was pointing and saw a man with a pencil thin mustache, like that of Clark Gable, sitting in front of the cabin door. Toan laughed to himself. *Aren't all Vietnamese mustaches like Clark Gable's?* He went up and introduced himself.

"I'm Dr. Vuong. Are you the boat owner?"

The man shrugged. "I'm a passenger."

Toan turned around and looked at the woman, who identified him as the owner. She gave him the go-ahead with just a wave of her hand. Toan looked back at the man. "You are the boat owner. What's your name?"

The man got very angry and started to gesture with his hands but never did admit he was the owner of the broken-down boat. "Hung, my name is Hung. I must tell you that the boat engine's out of order in the first place, the boat is so rotten. No way it will make the trip!"

He swung his arm and hit the edge of the boat, knocking off a piece of wood about a half meter long. The wooden shard splashed into the sea and just floated there.

"To tell the truth," Hung continued, "we'd better stay here until the constables get us. We'll only go to jail. If we try to sail this boat, for sure, we'll all die!"

Toan looked down at Vu and Dao, who were standing on each side. Toan's head dropped. He had never been an aggressive individual but now was different. He stepped toward Hung.

"I can't return, have to go. I'd rather swing from the end of a rope. If we can get to the international waters and are saved by a foreign ship, we'll survive. If not, my entire family members will jump into the sea to our deaths!"

Below deck, Toan's son, Vu heard what his father said and looked at Quynh Dao. "Are you going to jump to the sea to try to drown if the constables show up?"

Quynh Dao got a funny look on her face then frowned as though she had contemplated the question. She shook her head back and forth. "I'm not committing suicide. I can't swim, but I'm going to. Or try to."

Quynh Hoa walked up as Vu asked the question. She was more forceful. "Absolutely not. Mother and Father may not be willing to go back to Vietnam, but I'm not going to die at sea."

Vu matter-of-factly said to both. "We are going to make it. I just believe we are going to get out of here. Everything is going to be okay."

Toan gently pushed his way over to the engine room wthere a tanned young man stood. "Who's the owner of the boat? Do you know?"

He barely looked up. "No owner. I'm a passenger myself. Before leaving, the owner told me to be a pilot's aid, and a real pilot will take over. I have always sailed on rivers, never at sea."

Toan was very flustered with his answer. *Was Hung the owner of the Big Boat? Who'd fess up to owning this rickety thing anyway? At the moment it all seems irrelevant if the motor fails to start.* He turned and went back to his place inside the fish compartment. He had no more than settled in before someone came to collect money for the pilot. *The pilot? Why are we collecting for the pilot?* The person taking up the collection told him that some passengers had actually given ten to twenty US dollars. Toan felt compelled and dropped in a chi gold ring.

Another hour passed. Suddenly, the boat jolted as the engine restarted. This made Toan content. He quickly relaxed and fell back to sleep in those cramped quarters. After a short period of time, he was awakened again. This time he wasn't sure whether it was voices or because the boat had stopped. He got where he could see his watch; he had slept for two hours. Toan estimated that if the boat was moving at three to four kilometers per hour, slower than humans walk. He quickly calculated they may be ten kilometers from the Vietnam shoreline, just out of sight. He stepped out again and talked to several women on the deck of the ship. The consensus of opinion seemed to be that the pilot shut down the overheated engine so it would cool off. It seemed a logical solution. *We are still not out in international waters.*

With the boat floating lifeless at sea due to engine troubles, word circulated for everyone to hurry and get into the fish compartments. Toan looked around on the horizon. He didn't see any approaching boats, but someone must have. *Was it the Vietnamese Navy?* People scurried like rats to get into the compartments. Now, even Nha-Y, Quynh Trang, and Thanh hustled into their tiny compartment. It was stifling hot and a breath of air was a premium.

After a half hour, everyone was allowed back on deck. The pilot, Son, came over to explain to Toan that he believed they had been spotted by a nationalized fishing boat, likely with Vietnamese constables on board. Son assumed that since their boat was anchored near the shore with few men and a fishing net, they must have assumed this was a fishing boat and chosen not to inspect.

Toan and Nha-Y talked for a few minutes on the deck. Nha-Y decided to go check on the children. A sense of helplessness washed over Toan. He leaned backward on the side of the boat. He and his family were trapped, the boat's motor still not running. There was likely more than one nationalized fishing boat out in these waters. Would the next one stop and check their boat? *We cannot go back. They had to make it out of Vietnam or drown. Could I do that if the time came?* Time was creeping by so slowly everyone was looking around on the water searching for other ships.

Every three or four hours throughout the day, Son passed among the passengers with a five-gallon bucket of dirty river water. Each passenger got a cap full. *Who knows what is in that water, but what can we do?* Toan thought.

Around 5:00 p.m., the boat's motor was fired up again. This brought a cheer from all the passengers. Word circulated throughout the boat that some young man named Sum, with a pair of pincers and a screwdriver, had managed to fix the engine. Then another story about Sum circulated: Sum had attempted to escape before and had been caught a few times. He had just been released from jail a few months earlier. Sum was leaving this time with his ten-year-old nephew. Toan felt lucky to have Sum on the boat. *He may be our best bet for a successful escape.*

Eventually, the boat was gliding slowly along the surface of the water. Toan estimated they were going about four or five kilometers per hour. The boat's hull was old and in terrible shape. Sea water had been present since they boarded, and every time they stopped, more seeped into the lower level. Toan sat back and tried to relax but the stress and his condition, the consistent stomachache, kept him from eating anything, only taking sips of water to keep from dehydrating in the hot sun.

Still, he had to climb over the back of the boat to handle his bowel issues. At both ends, there were spaces where the passengers urinated and defecated, causing a very bad smell. Most of the young men and people in the cabin stepped across the boat roof to the stern to go to the bathroom. Toan had refrained from smoking cigarettes out of fear that he would run out. He had no idea when he would be able to find cigarettes again. But now he wanted one badly. He opened a pack of Craven A, tapped one out, lit it.

Just before midnight, everybody was ordered back into the fish compartment, as they were about to pass by Tho Chau Island, on which the constabulary had mounted a high-powered spotlight. It served two purposes: One was navigation of the sea while the other was to inspect the boats. Before they could even get to the island, the passengers were called back up on the deck.

Toan was worried they had been spotted. Miraculously, as their boat approached, a thick fog rolled in from the sea. It prevented the spotlight from penetrating the open deck. He felt very blessed and hoped this would be the last point to worry about the Vietnamese authorities.

Once they were past and out of sight of Tho Chau Island, the word circulated that they had reached international waters. There was great celebration and now everyone could come up on deck without concern. As part of the celebration, food and drinks were served, such as they were, but no one seemed to care. Toan, Vu, and Quynh Dao went up to pick up their share, including Quynh Hoa's rations. He was very careful what he ate, so as not to make his stomach situation worse.

The boat's engine seemed to get noisier. He was unsure whether it was his imagination or if they were pushing it harder. He slipped through the crowded deck to the cabin to see Nha-Y, Quynh Trang, and Thanh. Despite the dark of night, Toan and Nha-Y moved to the edge of the boat to watch the dolphins jumping out of the water as they followed and played alongside of the boat. It was exhilarating. This only lasted for a few minutes, as Toan started noticing oil slicks and broken up pieces of boards floating on the water. Must be from a wrecked or sunken ship. Wonder when?

Vu pushed his way through the crowded deck to his mother and father. He whispered to his father, "I overheard a conversation between the pilot, Son, and the nephew of Xoi, the boat owner's. This was after the engine stopped the first time. He told Son that he didn't believe their boat was seaworthy enough to make the trip to Thailand. He said they should each empty a water can, then use it as a buoy to assist their swim to shore. But they both claimed they were scared of drowning or being captured by the constables before they could cover the four to five kilometers to the beach. You need to watch them, Father."

The pilot, Son, saw Toan smoking a cigarette and came over and bummed one. Toan was reluctant to give any up but at the same time, he believed he had to attempt to keep the pilot happy. And his generosity earned him an immediate reward: He got to hold the throttle cord to the engine. He thought that was fun.

Around noon on the next day, about twenty young passengers, including Vu and Quynh Dao, were ordered to scoop out the water in the bottom of the boat that was continuously leaking in through a crack. By then Toan's stomach issues had deteriorated to the point that he was experiencing diarrhea about every thirty minutes to an hour. Each time, he had to slip through the crowd on the deck and crawl across the roof, squeezing through some more young men just sitting there. "Excuse me. Excuse me," he said as he bumped through them. All this before hanging over the side of the ship holding onto a pole while going to the bathroom. As a result, he became seasick from swinging off the back of the boat each time. He was afraid this condition could cause him to fall into the sea and drown.

Toan was exhausted and dehydrated as a result of the sun, stress, and his physical problems, yet all he could do was to return to the fish compartment. As a physician, he knew he needed a lot of things, but all that was available to him was an occasional sip of water and, possibly, sleep.

Chapter Twenty

Pirates

Gulf of Thailand

5:00 p.m., Thursday, March 27, 1980

Toan was startled awake by repeated shouts of "Pirates!" He glanced down at his watch. Toan gathered himself and struggled to get out of the fish compartment. Just as the boat lurched to an abrupt stop, tossing Toan forward. He managed to keep his feet and clambered up top. Once on deck, the engine still running, he quickly surveyed the boat and his surroundings. There it was, a huge fishing ship over fifty meters long, six meters high. A passenger was selected from their midst, by the name of Mr. Nhon, to represent all the passengers to board the 'pirate' boat. Quickly, the word circulated that the pirate ship was from a Thai fishing organization. While Toan had been selected as the spokesman for the boat, Mr. Nhon was fluent in the Thai language. Funny, Toan had never seen a fishing boat armed with machine guns. *Gives shooting fish in a barrel a whole different meaning.*

Mr. Nhon was hoisted onto the huge fishing ship with the machine guns.

After about fifteen minutes, Mr. Nhon was let back down from the pirate ship. He carried an edict from the "pirates." He stood and spoke as loudly as he could.

"The captain will have one of his compatriots walk among us with a large bowl to collect US dollars, gold, jewelry, and watches from each and every passenger. They're calling it a towing fee. Only when the bowl is filled will they tow our 'disabled' boat to Bangkok. As an incentive for the passenger's cooperation to pay, if anyone fails to cooperate now or if upon reaching Thailand any gold is found in their possession, that passenger or passengers will be thrown into the sea—after taking the valuable items."

The look of these Thai pirates put the fear of God into all the passengers.

After completing his announcement, Mr. Nhon looked up at the man leaning over from the Thai ship and waved his arm. Immediately, a Thai pirate was loaded into a fish net and lowered onto the Vietnamese ship. He had a large bucket in one hand while he held a fish net with the other. He was an intimidating individual. He started walking among the Vietnamese shouting at them in Thai. Everyone was dropping gold rings, watches, US dollars into the bucket. He would snarl at some of the passengers. He must have believed they were holding out or he wanted to intimidate those escapees from whom he had not yet collected. His actions got immediate results and did in fact inspire anyone standing nearby to comply when the bucket was held in front of them. Toan went into the fish compartment to get his children and emphatically stated, "Hand over all the gold rings and dollars, including what's been stitched into your clothing. It's for your own protection."

When the Thai pirate stepped in front of him, Toan pulled out a one-ChI ring and forty US dollars and dropped them in the bucket. The pirate looked down at his wrist. Toan realized he had forgotten to remove his Omega watch. This was most difficult, as it had been a momentum his father had given to him when he had traveled to France. But he slipped it off his wrist and dropped it in the bucket, too. Finally, after making his rounds, Mr. Nhon returned to the Thai pirate ship with the Thai pirate.

When he was lowered back to the Vietnamese boat, Mr. Nhon announced loud enough to be heard by all the passengers, "They collected some three Tael of gold, a few hundred dollars, and three watches. Our ransom must have been sufficient."

Toan watched the Thai pirate climb back into the large fishnet and motioned for Mr. Nhon to join him. He did not need to ask twice. All Toan could think about was he did not to be want thrown into the sea; he assumed that feeling was shared by the balance of the passengers. As soon as the two men stepped onto the Thai fishing boat, the captain stepped toward the pirate with the bucket. He turned back to Mr. Nhon and began gesturing and speaking loudly in Thai. Toan watched intently as they talked and wished he knew the language better. Still, he could tell things didn't seem to be going well. After a fifteen-to twenty-minute conversation, Mr. Nhon was lowered back down to the Vietnamese ship.

Again, he stood and spoke loud enough for everyone to hear. "The captain wants all women and children to move to the ship in order to diminish the weight in our boat. The men should stay here."

Several Thai pirates lowered themselves down to the ship with a big rope to tie it off to the pole at the bow of boat for towing. Simultaneously, the Thai pirates started to move women and children from the boat to the larger pirate ship. After about a half an hour everything was set. Three members of Toan's family, Nha-Y, Quynh Trang, and Thanh, were transferred to the pirate ship. Toan wondered why the remainder of his family—Quynh Dao and Quynh Hoa plus sister Hong and Ms. Lien—stayed on board the smaller ship. *Very strange.*

The Thai pirate ship started forward with a lurch, and the rope was pulled tight immediately, the pole making a cracking noise that shook the tiny boat. At first, Toan was afraid the boat would come apart, but within a minute their boat was being towed about ten times faster than they had achieved before, easily forty kilometers per hour. To avoid the pole being broken, some young passengers took turns holding it all together, rope, pole, and bow.

About an hour later, late in the afternoon, the pirate ship came to an abrupt stop. The captain ordered foods, drinks, even cigarettes, brought down to the Vietnamese ship. Everybody was pleased. Toan was starting to feel better physically; he tried to relax just a little bit. He ventured for the first time in days to eat a little bit of food. He was even more pleased to get some more cigarettes, as he had only a few left after having shared them with the Vietnamese boat pilot. In spite of his family being in two groups, Toan was beginning to believe that everything was going to turn out okay. They might actually make it to Banglok without another incident. He was able to catch another little nap in his roomier fish compartment as the rocking of the ship on the water put him into a deep sleep. During the night, Toan only awoke up long enough to smoke another cigarette.

Just before daylight the Thai ship stopped abruptly, jarring everyone, especially those who were sleeping. A young Thai pirate boarded the smaller boat to check and see if anyone had guns, knives, grenades, or any kind of weapon. Naturally, everyone on board denied having any. On his way back through the crowd, he announced that the captain was going to cut them loose and leave with the women and children. The captain believed they were all holding out valuables. Then he picked up a bucket and started to collect some more valuables. This time, everyone had to pull out their pockets and open their hands in his presence.

Quynh Dao was standing on the deck watching the Thai pirate go from individual to individual. The pirate would ask in Thai, "Empty your pocket then open your hands."

Quynh Dao was far enough away that she was certain he could not see her. She discreetly took the money out of her inseam and slipped it inside her trouser belt. She reasoned that he didn't speak Vietnamese since she had not heard him do so yet. Although she was taking a big risk, she slipped her little finger inside the chi gold ring and hid it in her mouth.

When the pirate stepped in front of her. He asked, "Do you understand what I am saying?"

She shook her head no.

The Thai pirate tapped her pocket with his left hand.

She slipped her hands in her pockets and turned them inside out then held her open hands at her side face up.

He barked at her in Thai. "Is that all you have?"

She shook her head up hard up and down, yes. Perhaps too hard as the ring rattled in her mouth. She was sure he heard the ring clanging in her teeth.

The pirate looked her up and down for a month, so long that she got scared. Then he stepped to the next individual.

Quynh Dao remained fixed in her position, but she felt relieved.

Once he had finished checking everybody out, he returned to the Thai fishing ship. Many young men had concealed their gold and money and did not give it away. Ms.

Lien had her money wrapped in a towel and threw it to the water in the bottom of the boat.

Shortly after the pirate returned to the Thai ship, they brought around food and water for everybody on the Vietnamese ship. Quynh Dao was so happy. When she'd arrived at the Big Boat she was not feeling well, the beginnings of seasickness. Stuffed into the stinky fish compartment, with her father on one side and Quynh Hoa on the other, no air to breathe and unable to move, the seasickness had gotten progressively worse. She was seasick for a whole day. She eventaully couldn't hold back anymore and threw up. There was nothing in her stomach: no food, no water, only bile.

After finishing her rice, hung sour fish soup, and water, Quynh Dao looked up at her father. "This is the best meal I have ever had."

Her father just smiled at her.

Then Quynh Dao signaled for her father to lower his head. She cupped her left hand between her mouth and his ear. "I saved my ring and the U.S. dollars."

This brought an even bigger smile to his face.

They sailed through the night in the direction of the Thai coast.

Saturday, March 28, 1980

The Thai pirates stopped two more times to feed them steamed rice with other foods and drinks. After the second stop, at about 5:00 p.m., pirates brought fuel and water over to dump the fuel in the tank and water in the rickety radiator. Then several pirates assisted the women and children back over to the smaller boat. One of them went up to Mr. Nhon. "It is time for us to go fishing," the pirate said. "We can't tow the boat any farther." Then he pointed. "Look, the Thai shore is there some dozen miles ahead, just sail straight."

As one of the pirates took off the large rope tied to the bow, the others on the Thai ship dropped fishing nets. No sooner did the pirate jump back onto their ship than their engine was started and they headed off fishing, going out of sight in a matter of minutes.

Chapter Twenty-One

Real Pirates and the Liberian Freighter

Gulf of Thailand

Late afternoon, Friday, March 28, 1980

Pilot Son stood there on the front of the boat watching the Thai fisherman pull away. One of the passengers went up to him. Toan could not hear what was being said, but there was a lot of arm gesturing. When the passenger walked away, Pilot Son went over and started working hard to restart that old engine.

Over the next couple of hours, Toan was certain he heard at least a hundred attempts to restart. *Nothing.* By then the darkness of the evening had begun to set in, and a rush of anxiety overcame Toan. He got out of the fish compartment to go up on deck and see why the engine was not starting. He squeezed his way to the engine compartment.

The word was the engine that propelled the boat was actually designed for milling rice, and it leaked from overwork and old age. He watched Pilot Son and other young men take turns holding a wooden handle on a round block of stone about one meter in diameter and struggling to make it turn around. It reminded Toan of the way drivers used to crank up car engines back in the 1930s. He was very disappointed, turned and slowly walked back to the fish compartment. *It is going to be night, and we are drifting off in the Gulf of Thailand. This is not a good situation.*

Night set in. Toan was overwhelmed with a desperation so intense he could not sleep. *Could we get this close and still fail?* Constant noises came from the repeated attempts to restart the boat's engine. Just past midnight, Pilot Son entered the bottom compartment. "Does anyone have a match box? I need it to fix the engine."

Toan pulled out an empty box of matches and handed it to him.

Son took it, looked at it. "Sum is back working on the engine. He needs a box cover to stop an oil leak." Son stepped out of the compartment and closed the door.

Toan followed him out of the fish compartment long enough to smoke one of his last cigarettes. As he was finished, he glanced at the horizon in every direction. He was looking for pirate ships. Fortunately, he did not see any. Then he looked up at the night sky to see the stars: The view was more spectacular then he'd ever seen.

He thought of his younger days. He'd been a practicing Buddhist all his life, and he remembered his mother used to pray daily from their home. Often, she would take Toan, his brothers and sisters to the temple to pray during Tet festivals and funerals. It was time for him to pray. It was his only hope for solace. Toan imagined himself walking into the Buddhist Temple in Hanoi accompanying his mother. Now he could almost smell the incense burning, as he walked through the Bell Tower to the Drum Tower then to the Hall of the Heavenly Kings before entering the main worship hall where the statue of the Buddha sat. Instinctively, he began to pray a prayer he had learned as a child, "Nam mô đại từ bi, cứu khổ cứu nạn, quảng đại linh cảm Bạch-Y Quán-Thế Âm Bồ-Tát . . ." He continued to do so without interruption until morning.

As morning broke, a sense of peace came over Toan. He was relieved they made it through the night without being assaulted again by pirates. Reflecting on his family's escape, he remembered the risks of attempting to escape he'd cited at the beginning: Nine parts dead, one part alive, he'd said. He decided he needed to up the odds; it now seemed to be ninety-nine parts dead, one part alive. Circumspect about his own sense of peace, he believed if all the family members would die at the same time, it would be all right with him.

This time of year, the sea was relatively calm when the boat was moving. However, if it was stopped, it was swung by waves listing in every direction. *This boat might capsize. Death by drowning would be horrible.* Faithfully, he continued praying to Buddha, despite his dizziness. Toan tried leaning against the side of the hull and closed his eyes to try to suppress his sea-sickness. From time to time, he would open his eyes to check on Quynh Hoa, who was just lying there, while Vu and Quynh Dao continuously scooped sea water from the boat bottom. He was proud of how diligent their efforts were.

Suddenly, the boat's engine sprung to life, bringing a round of cheers. Toan marveled at Sum. First, he had repaired the engine with a pair of pincers and a screwdriver. Now he added an empty box of matches to the two tools to get it running. *Amazing.* Fifteen hours of persistent work, and he got the engine running again. The man was a savior. Toan took some personal satisfaction that his prayer and likely those of others on the boat had produced the miracle. Toan immediately stood up and went to the cabin to see Nha-Y. His hope had been restored.

Around noon, someone at the front of the boat spotted a large sea-going vessel on the horizon. It was on a course to pass close to their tiny boat. All the passengers on their slow-moving boat began to wave and yell at the large ship. Some went so far as to hang clothes and a blanket on a pole that they raised for the sailors to see and come to their rescue. However, the sea-going vessel continued its course, completely ignoring the refugees' boat. A huge disappointment. The refugee's boat continued to putter along. Then, one of the passengers spotted a derrick on the horizon. Pilot Son steered the boat in its direction only to discover it was abandoned. With that he steered back on the previous course for the still unseen Thailand shore.

As the day continued, the heat was stifling. Toan wiped his brow as he tried to move around on the overcrowded boat. He bumped into one of the passengers, who poked Toan in the side and pointed toward an object on the horizon. Toan continued to push his way back to Pilot Son, who changed course toward what appeared to be a ship.

For several hours, they slowly motored toward what appeared to be an ocean-going freighter. As they got close enough to identify some markings, they saw the flag flying on the bridge, indicating it was a Liberian ship. When they were finally alongside, it was huge. Likely a hundred meters long. The part above the water line was about ten meters. Since Toan had been selected as spokesman for the passengers, they insisted he board the boat to talk to the ship's captain. The sailors lowered down a big rope, Toan attempted to climb up, but his feet could not reach the hull. He was only able to climb a couple of meters.

One of the sailors leaning over the side shouted, "Down! Down quick! Can't go up!"

This scared Toan, who was already frustrated at his inability to climb. So he did as the sailor commanded and climbed back down to the deck of the refugee ship. Next, the sailors lowered a big cargo net down to the boat and waved for Toan to get in and they would hoist him up.

Swinging back and forth, Toan was quickly brought to the top of the freighter, it landed on a cabin, which was about two meters above the main deck. He looked around and spotted a white man standing on the deck with his hands on his hips. Toan assumed he was the captain. He was in such a hurry to meet the man, he jumped down to the deck. He landed awkwardly, severely spraining his ankle. That would not deter him, and he limped over to the assumed captain, excited and out of breath. In his best limited English, he lied to make their story more dramatic and hopefully compassionate: "We have been at sea for ten days. Our boat is broken, barely running. We are short on gasoline and engine oil. We are out of food and water. I requested to come aboard your ship so that we all can come aboard and you could take us to a foreign country."

The captain folded his arms across his chest and said in poor English. "My ship does not fly under any country's flag."

Toan looked up at the Liberian flag flying and raised his eyebrows as the captain continued to talk.

The captain continued. "She is a cargo ship to export Thai goods to Japan. If you like, I will permit all to board, but only to get you back to Vietnam on my way to Japan."

This was the last thing Toan wanted to hear. He continued his bargaining. "Then take us to Japan."

The captain shook his head no, then added, "I will give you everything you need. Your boat was sailing, in spite of its slow speed. It will get to the Thai shore in few hours."

Before Toan could say another word, the captain pivoted and walked away. He barked out orders to his men to lower plenty of boxes to the refugee boat, then lastly two big bags. Immediately, the sailors started to manipulate the ship's derricks to the designated items to the little boat. One of the sailors pointed at Toan, then pointed at the net that carried the boxes. Toan got the message, he was to return to the boat in the same manner he came up . . . in the net. When the net with the boxes was set down, the refugee boat rocked and almost capsized. One of the two big boxes had rice and the other, salt.

Toan decided the only thing he could do was limp back to the fish compartment to rest and take weight off his ankle. No sooner had he settled into the fish compartment, when he heard mumbling outside the door.

"Hey! What's the direction to sail! Everyone on the boat's about to drown. Death to all!"

He was too disappointed in himself to look and see what that was all about. He had failed to negotiate safe passage for his family and the balance of the passengers. He had a task to achieve and he'd let everyone down. All he could do was lay down and close his eyes. He drifted off to sleep from exhaustion.

Within a couple of minutes, Vu could hear the boat's engine running, and the boat lurched forward with a hard turn that nearly caused it to capsize. Before the Liberian ship had moved more than several hundred meters, he saw several medium-size speed boats appear from the opposite side of the freighter and approach at a high rate of speed. Someone on the front boat shouted, "Thai pirates!"

Vu swiftly spun around, as there were ten pirate boats encircling their boat from different directions. One of the pirates' boats slipped alongside the refugee boat. As the boat moved past, it slowed down enough for one of the two pirates to jump onto their boat with a rope in hand. His first act was to intimidate the Vietnamese closest to him, gesturing wildly with his hands. Needless to say, those closest to the Thai pirate backed off. The Thai pirate quickly moved to the front of the boat and started to tie off the rope to the refugee boat. Vu watched as the speed boat the pirate had jumped from moved rapidly in front and started to take out the slack on the rope. Vu noticed a Vietnamese moving toward him. It was the man that his father had told him was Sum, the man who had repeatedly repaired the engine.

Sum shouted, "Give me a knife!" hoping that someone still had one.

One of the younger passengers produced a cleaver and tossed it to Sum. Sum ran up and started chopping the rope. By the second wack, the Thai pirate charged Sum, who from a crutched position side-kicked the Thai pirate. Staggered, the pirate stumbled to attack, and Sum side-kicked him again. This caused him to lose his balance temporarily, but more importantly, it caused his sarong to fall to the ground. The Thai pirate dropped both hands rapidly to pull it up. In that instant, Sum charged and delivered the final front snap kick sending the Thai pirate head over heels backwards into the sea.

Sum hacked one more time at the rope. Simultaneously, Pilot Son pushed the throttle forward while he steered the boat away from the pirate's boats in the direction of the Liberian freighter. While their moves were quick and effective, it did not get them out of immediate danger as there were other Thai pirate boats circling. Several of the Vietnamese screamed and shrieked. Pilot Son had the boat going as fast as it would possibly go. Vu felt the vibration, he believed the boat would come apart or the engine would give out they were going so hard.

The race was on. Could the rickety Vietnamese boat make it to the Liberian freighter before more Thai pirates in speed boats could get to them?

Vu looked back at the Liberian freighter and saw two ferry boats from the Liberian freighter approaching their boat. Pilot Son aimed between the two ferry boats. At this point Vu didn't care if it came apart as he knew it was their only chance of escaping the Thai pirates.

The boat made a sharp turn and nearly capsized. It went from dead stop to maximum speed, jolting everyone forward. Toan was jostled around in the fish compartment as he tried hard to get up to look outside. Once back out on deck, he saw that their boat was rapidly approaching the Liberian freighter from both sides. One of the passengers ran up to Toan and shouted.

"We barely got one hundred meters from the freighter! We were immediately encircled by ten pirate boats. I am sure they were going to rob and kill us!"

The excited passenger continued telling him a pirate had had a rope lassoed to the pole at the stem of their boat and had jumped in the boat. Then, Sum shouted, "Give me a knife!"

A young passenger threw him a large knife. The excited passenger continued to tell the story of what had happened. He waved his arms around gesturing.

"Sum caught it in one hand then ran to the front of the boat. In two quick chops, Sum cut the rope in two. When the pirate stood up on the boat's edge and started toward Sum, his sarong fell down around his feet, the moment he reached down to pull it back up, Sum bravely ran forward, gave him a karate kick, which knocked him off the bow and into the sea."

Hearing this, Toan realized he must have passed out into a deep sleep. *How long was I out? How could all of this happen and me not hear it?*

The sailors on the ship must have observed the pirate boats. Toan realized how lucky they were. If they had gotten much farther away from the freighter, they would have likely fallen to the pirates. There was no way their rickety boat could have escaped.

Once they were secured by the Liberian ship, the captain gave his permission to let all the Vietnamese refugees board the ferry boat tethered to the massive freighter. Toan wondered why the captain of the freighter changed his mind. He had to be aware the pirates were close by. Whatever reason he had second thoughts, he likely saved their lives. Now was he going to grant the request to take them ashore. Before climbing into the ferry boat, Toan went over to pilot Son and several of the young passengers, including Sum. He whispered so no one else could hear: "Destroy the engine and put some holes in the hull of the boat."

Pilot Son and Sum agreed.

"This is the only way to stay on the ferry boats," Toan said quietly. "If we have to go back to this old boat, we will be punished by the pirates. We need to make sure that once we are on the ferry boat, we can not leave it."

Toan took two steps and stopped, adding, "Don't forget to make sure our belongings and the goods the Liberian freighter left us are moved to the ferry boat."

As night was setting in, Toan asked to talk to the Liberian captain again, but the sailors denied him. However, they did send down some food, water, frozen sandwich bread, and canned pineapple. When several passengers heard about the rejection, they approached Toan and told him to offer some gold and US dollars to tow the ferry boat to a deserted place and leave them in shallow water. The passengers wanted to be able to paddle ashore.

If Toan was going to bargain with the gold and US dollars, he had to first learn what the situation was regarding the Thai government. He was assured the Thai government would not accept boat people from Liberia, which disappointed him. Once again, he'd failed to negotiate a solution for his fellow Vietnamese refugees.

Off in the distance, he could see another boat approaching. Once the boat pulled alongside, one of their passengers shouted they had tried to enter Thailand but were chased away by the Thai Coast Guard. They thought about trying another place, most likely Malaysia, about thirty kilometers away. Toan got the impression they were just hanging around to see if they could join them. They told Toan's group that they came from the Ca Mau province in Vietnam, plus there may be another one hundred passengers from that same area, escaping behind them. Despite Toan's veiled attempts to get them to move on, the boat remained.

Well into the night, Toan heard the sound of one—or maybe two—other boats approaching. Eyes sweeping across the dark water, he could see two motorboats with high intensity spotlights. One of the boats went to their old disabled boat. After a few minutes, they pulled alongside of the ferry and tied off. The other boat remained about fifty meters out. Several of the men stepped onto their boat; they were Thai Coast Guard officers. The highest-ranking officer demanded, in rough Vietnamese, to speak to the spokesman for Toan's group. He stepped forward.

The Thai Coast Guard officer asked if he spoke Thai, which he didn't. The Coast Guard began interrogating him anyway. The Thai officer advised him they had received a call from the Liberian captain notifying them of the attempted attack by the pirates and came to investigate.

After speaking with Toan for a few minutes, they interrogated several other passengers, including Sum. Once everybody's stories were corroborated and they had inspected the disabled boat, they went back to their boat and talked among themselves. Toan watched the officer he had spoken to pick up their radio microphone and talk into it. He wished he knew what was being said.

Time passed. The Coast Guard remained. Nothing seemed to be happening.

Then Toan saw another set of spotlights approaching. Slowly, it drew close enough to identify—a very large Thai Coast Guard pontoon boat. They positioned it in front. One of the Coast Guard personnel returned to the ferry, caught a thrown rope and secured it. They tied off another to the broken-down old boat. The Coast Guard officer stepped back on board to tell Toan that they were to be towed to Pattani. Then they towed both boats toward the Thai seashore. As soon as he returned to the Coast Guard speedboat, he signaled the pontoon boat to go.

After a half hour of towing, Toan finally relaxed, his mind clearing. Land was in front of them; his family had escaped the communist Vietnamese. At last. Part of his relief came from a strange sight of the old boat and its broken engine being towed by a Thai Coast Guard pontoon boat. A feeling near euphoria raced over him. He'd never experienced it in his lifetime. *Was this like being resurrected from the dead? Relief because all my family survived? It's a miracle!*

The trip that Toan had characterized as nine parts dead, one part alive he now believed this to be more precisely a ninety-nine parts dead, one part alive trip. Nha-Y composed a poem that memorialized their life-and-death trip titled:

Rạch Giá

Túng thế cùng dướng cũng phải chui,
Vùa may Rạch Giá găp anh Xồi.
Máy hư, nước ngập, tài công thiếu,
Tàu mục, nguới đông, vào biển khơi!
Nủa chuyến vuợt biên nhờ 'cướp' Thái,
Thâu đêm sủa máy tạ ơn Trời!
Chú Sum dạo ấy giờ đâu nhỉ?
Đạp cuớp, sủa tàu... công mấy muời!

Chapter Twenty-Two

First Refugee Camp in Thailand

Outside Pattani, Thailand

March 29, 1980

As the boat was towed past the Thai shoreline, the same Coast Guard officer—the high ranking one—walked over to Toan. "The Liberian captain told us he had planned to tow your group to Japan. However, when the Ca Mau boat passengers were added, he understood it was beyond his limit to safely attempt to take that many refugees to Japan. He did not have enough supplies. He was forced to send a message to the Thai Coast Guard station at Pattani, the nearest coastal city."

It was not long before the Coast Guard vessel stopped close to the mouth of a river. Toan picked out some slices of pineapple from a cooler. They were quite delicious.

He lit a cigarette. All the passengers from his boat were very happy. There seemed to be a sense of reflection, some people leisurely smoking cigarettes, while others ate candies or fruit. They all appeared to share a common feeling: back to life!

A Coast Guard officer walked among the refugees and announced, "If anyone wishes to send a letter or telegram back home, he can do so, but you have to provide money for postage."

Several of the passengers accepted his offer. However, he couldn't take their money because he did not carry small change.

As night set in, the ferry boat re-started up the river. Toan looked out the back of the ferry in time to see ten-meter high waves rolling in from the sea. He realized there had been no way their original Big Boat could have ever been able to circumnavigate the Bay of Thailand seas. Surely that overloaded, leaky craft would have come apart and everyone would have drowned.

After slowly trawling up the river for about an hour, the Coast Guard boat landed the ferry boat, and all the passengers were ordered to disembark onto the riverbank. The younger passengers bounded off the ferry, hustling toward a nearby store to pick up cartons of cigarettes, bags of coffee, or boxes of canned goods, sugar, and other dry goods.

Toan's family was one of the last two to exit the ferry. Before he got out of the boat, Toan tapped Quynh Dao on the back. "Better give me the chi gold ring and the cash."

Quynh Dao discreetly slipped her hand inside her pocket and handed him the items.

Since his ankle was badly swollen and still wouldn't bear his weight, he limped over to the head of the other family trying to help Vu and Quynh Dao carry the big bags of rice and sugar. His ankle was so bad, he needed help getting off the boat. With strangers under each shoulder, he began the climb away from the riverbank.

There were several Thai civilians in the vicinity of the refugees watching them as they disembarked the ferry. A woman maybe in her early fifties approached Toan's family and attempted to give Quynh Trang a piece of paper. *What was that?* Toan thought. *Was that money?*

Toan shouted at Quynh Trang to refuse it. He had heard stories of child abduction in Thailand. Toan got the two strangers to move faster as soon as they were on nearly flat ground so he could protect his wife and children as quickly as possible. They drew together and all hugged. He looked around to make sure that sisters Hong and Lien were still close by.

Waiting for them were Thai police officers who ordered everyone to make two parallel lines. They stood in the same place in line for a little more than an hour before, finally, two trucks pulled into the park. The police dispersed the Thais then ordered the refugees into the truck beds. Once again, Toan's family and the family who had disembarked the ferry with them were the last to climb in. Toan was struggling after standing so long, trying not to put weight on his ankle, but he managed to work his way into the back of the truck bed. Again, the other family helped Vu and Quynh Dao push the bags of rice and sugar aboard the trucks. After everyone and everything was in, Toan learned the other family's last name was Hop.

As the two trucks pulled away from the curb, Toan and Mr. Hop were pushed so closely together they had no choice but to begin a conversation. Toan learned the Hop family story: They had escaped with their daughter Quynh Giao, who they called Ki Keo. Their older son, who was about ten years old, had already made it to the United States and was living with his maternal grandfather. Hop nodded as he said, "This is going to be instrumental in our quest to get to the United States."

The two trucks passed through the small town of Pattani on their way into the interior of Thailand. Ten minutes or so on the other side of Pattani, the trucks turned into an area enclosed by low barbed wire. They went through the main gate and up a road before stopping in front of a brick house.

Toan leaned out over the edge of the truck bed to see more. Beyond the dwelling was what looked like rows of tin-roofed, tile-paved barns. A man came out of the brick house and waved vigorously for everyone to get out of the trucks. He ushered them to the barn. The Thai man randomly assigned spaces on the floor for the families. Toan, his family, and the two sisters set up next to the Hop family. A little while later, all the belongings were brought to their area. The belongings of Toan and his family had been reduced to five small handbags.

Shortly, another round of trucks pulled in with the Ca Mau refugees.

Late in the evening, as everybody was finally settled into the large barn, a policeman brought a kerosene lamp and hung it from a pillar in the center. The light was very dim. In broken Vietnamese, he advised everyone that there was a well near the brick house. He would show the way to anyone who wished to take a bath. Since it was dark and everyone seemed exhausted, there were no takers. Toan and his family began to bed down on the floor to sleep.

These conditions were not great by any stretch, Toan mused as he lay down to sleep, but he was no longer under communist rule. He reached into his pocket and fingered the chi gold ring. He set his priorities: He had to keep his family safe in this refugee camp, and he had to find a sponsor in the United States so his family could legally immigrate.

Starting first thing the next day, Toan talked and studied with others to learn what he could about the Pattani transit refugee camp. Due to his lack of mobility he could not explore like he wished. He was told by one of the elders from another family, who had been there a while, it had previously been an old cattle farm. The housing for the refugees, such as it was, consisted of two barns with paved floors, tin roofs, and brick pillars. There were ropes to separate each into two halves. Each barn was about thirty meters long and ten meters wide. The paved floor, broken and cracked, was maybe twenty centimeters higher than the ground. The camp was surrounded by grasses and random bushes.

The camp was assigned twenty-four hour security, seven days a week. One of three Thai police officers, Cham Run, acted friendly toward Toan. He offered to help Toan's family with selling gold, exchanging money, and sending letters to relatives or other contacts in foreign countries. The policeman's statement gave Toan great relief, as the police officer must have assumed they still had valuables with which to bargain. Fortunately, word had not circulated that Toan and his family had been robbed, including his cherished stamp collection. Toan knew he had to keep it that way. Yet every single time Cham saw him, he offered to take them into Pattani to sell gold rings or exchange US dollars for baht, at the exchange rate of twenty baht for one US dollar.

One of the few items of value Toan still had was the ring that Quynh Dao had put in her mouth instead of turning it over to the pirates. Toan was holding it back as he believed it could be the ring that would lead to freedom.

Sunday, April 13, 1980, two weeks later

Local markets, set up outside the camp, opened up very early every morning for families to get their produce for their daily meals. Early most mornings, Vu and Quynh Dao woke up hungry; it seemed to Vu like they had been hungry for years.

Until their father's ankle healed, they were his eyes and ears around the camp. Their task was to get sufficient rice and dried fish for meals, every day.

Toan's family responsibility had grown to a total of nine: Besides Nha-Y's sister and her friend it now included two of Toan's friends, Hai and Van, who had been on the original Big Boat. Considering the market's limitations of ten small fish, it was hard enough to provide filling meals. Toan and his family had been rewarded for their struggles to carry the hundred-kilogram bag of rice from the Liberian freighter, and they used it to barter for food and other items. Other members in the refugee camp had carried items from the ferry boats, such as dried foods, coffee, and cigarettes. Their father taught his family not only how to barter but how to share in their little community. Everyone benefited from the good barter exchanges.

Once they got familiar with the grounds and the markets, they did not always come straight back to their family stake. They went walking around the fenced-in area, exploring for something to do. One day, in a total state of boredom Vu talked Quynh Dao into walking along beside him as he paced off the area to which they were confined. He believed it was much like prisoners stepping out of their cells. Quynh Dao reluctantly agreed, and they learned the grounds were one hundred meters wide, by their estimation—and sixty meters deep. This was all they could find to do. Because there was no light, except of course the stinky kerosene lamp, they would sit around in their family area telling stories until it was time to go to bed . . . very early every single night.

The one place the adventurous Vu did not explore was the area against the back fence: the elevated boards over the ditches used as the toilets. Since they had left their grandfather's home, everyone in his family had adapted to different "styles" of bathrooms, but this one might have been the most humiliating.

They were not as interested in exploring on days when it had rained. The dirt road became very muddy, and in their sandals, it was very slick and they could not afford to drop any of their family's food on the way back. It seemed to Vu that he and Quynh Dao were always making trips up to the well behind the farm house, either to get water for everyone to wash or water to do the cooking.

Several different evenings, Vu had snooped around the farmhouse to see the tile-roofed brick house of the Thai family that lived in there. However, he was never able to learn anything about them.

Once Toan was finally able to hobble around among those in the large barn, he learned many things. He found Mr. Thinh, who was barracked on one side of their living space and had come from the Ca Mau boat. He had somehow managed to bring a coffee maker through their escape process, which Toan was allowed to borrow. *He probably took it from the ferry boat. It was so good getting a hot cup of coffee again.* He had to plan his trips among the residents of the camp carefully, as they all still only had one change of clothes; therefore, for a period of time every other day, Toan would have to wear his wife's pants. *As soon as I get on my feet, we are going to purchase some more clothing.*

During the past two weeks, two more boats of Vietnamese refugees from Ca Mau had arrived. The local police escorted in some seventy to eighty refugees. The first group included several individuals and families that Toan had been previously acquainted with in Vietnam: Dang and Lam, a teacher and a former American employee. With Lam was his son, Minh—a nurse whose real name was Dam Viet Trung— and Uong, who claimed to be a doctor and was accompanied by his wife and little boy.

The last group of thirty refugees came into camp, and their predicament was dire. They had been robbed literally down to their underwear. Among them was Dr. Phan Van Vong, who had worked at a clinic in Saigon. This made Toan concerned and compassionate for them; he sought out Cham Run.

Cham Run folded his arms across his chest and emphatically replied, "The circumstances surrounding your boat need to be investigated since it had been brought to land by the Coast Guard."

Toan stared at him for a minute trying to process his answer. *What the hell is he talking about? That has nothing to do with the circumstances I just presented.*

Due to the lack of outside influences, such as radios or televisions, this Vietnamese community had become very friendly. Toan became acquainted with several families from their boat besides just the Hop family. The first family was that of Mr. Thinh, a former employee of the Americans. He had come with his wife and child. Another family consisted of Mrs. Tra, whose husband had already settled in the United States, and her daughter. Then there was two individuals, Hai and Van, who would often invite Toan and Hop to come over to their place to drink tea, smoke cigarettes, and chat. Later, that group was joined by Dang, Minh, and Uong. Minh used to come to Toan's place every night, and Toan would always make a friendly gesture since they were both former military: "Officers, you're invited to have a cup of tea." All of them often chatted late into the night.

On rare occasions, Hai and Van invited only Toan to join them to sneak through the fence and get to the Thai house outside the refugee camp. They would pay the owner to fix a dish and buy alcohol for the three of them. Since this was a personal treat, Toan refused to use the gold ring to pay for any of these luxuries.

One night when Van was visiting with the Vuong family, he discreetly asked Toan, "Can Vu crawl through the fence and pick up some rau ngot leaves for soup or cut rau muong to boil?"

This was not the only request for Toan's children; Mrs. Hop had asked that Quynh Dao get outside the fence to pick up veggies. Toan consulted with Nha-Y and she approved, so he spoke with his two children. They readily agreed to conduct their clandestine act. They both knew it would provide more them to eat and be different than their regular menu of fish and rice.

Soon, the authorities granted permission for the young people to leave the confines of the camp. One day those industrious youth drained a ditch that they could fill with water and fish. As a result of their adventure, they collected enough fish and shrimp to share with their families.

A little more than a week after Toan's conversation with Cham Run, the most destitute of the refugees were transferred by the police to the Songkhla refugee camp. It was better equipped to handle their sorrowful condition.

About a month after Toan's family had arrived at the camp, where some two hundred refugees now lived, a French doctor from the Songkhla camp came to physically examine some of them. He had been sent by Doctors without Borders to conduct examinations of the refugees at the infirmary. As soon as he discovered that Toan was a physician who could speak French, he asked, "Would you be willing to conduct consultations and treat the refugees in Pattani?"

Toan replied, "Of course." Then he discreetly continued, "Could you cash a check I received from my sister Oanh for fifty US dollars? It was delivered by the Thai police."

Several days later, the French doctor returned not only with Toan's fifty US dollars but with medical instruments and medicine so Toan could better conduct his exams.

As time passed, the children got very familiar with the layout of the refugee camp and began to venture outside its confines. At first it was to use the bathroom. They decided that the dug trench was not good enough, and any place out in the sparsely wooded area was superior.

Quynh Hoa always had boys chasing after her. Usually, she ignored their attention. But due to boredom, occasionally, she would talk to a couple of them inside the refugee camp. Not to the point of letting anything get too serious. There were several occasions were Quynh Hoa had attracted the attention of a Thai boy from a nearby farm outside the camp. However, in order to not draw attention to her occasional slipping outside from her mother and father to visit this young man, she took Quynh Dao with her. Quynh Dao loved it because, being the tomboy she was, she could go and climb the fruit trees and eat fresh fruit while Quynh Hoa would visit the young suitor.

By late May 1980, Toan and his family had been in the Pattani refugee camp for about three months. He was becoming disgruntled. Some refugees who had arrived after their boat had been transferred out of the camp, but all fifty-four from Toan's group were still in the camp. He went to question Cham Run about why that was so.

Strangely, once again, the policeman replied, "The circumstances surrounding your boat need to be investigated since it had been brought to land by the Coast Guard." Then Run stared at Toan. "Perhaps your group should be sent back to Vietnam."

Once again, Cham's canned response puzzled Toan. He walked away. *Maybe he's looking for a bribe. I wonder if he would prevent us from getting out of here if he doesn't get paid. Is he saying these things to other residents here? I have to be very careful on my next step.*

Several days later, when the friendly French doctor came to check on Toan and the other refugees, there was the opportunity Toan was looking for. He asked, "I need a favor. I need you to discreetly check on our status when you get back to Songkhla. Can you do that?"

Chapter Twenty-Three

Out of Pattani to Songkhla

Songkhla refugee camp, Thailand

June, 1980

The last couple of weeks had been a whirlwind for the Vuong family. They had finally gotten out of the Pattani refugee camp and made it to Songkhla, where there were better living conditions. Toan's conversation with his new friend, the French doctor, had yielded positive results. The French doctor's inquiry had put the ball in motion and, miraculously, all nine members of his family had been moved. Toan's family settled in, both Toan and Nha-Y getting comfortable with letting their older children, Quynh Hoa, Vu, and Quynh Dao, move about the grounds unsupervised.

The Songkha refugee camp was a clear upgrade from Pattani. There were more activities available to the children, including schooling. They resided was in one of more than ten tin-roofed houses, which were like small warehouses with long platforms for beds. At the end of each was a bath and restroom. Each family was assigned a lot.

During the check-in process, Toan was told each of the houses were separated in two parts where as many as one hundred refugees could sleep. Before they settled into their assigned space, they exchanged lot assignments with Dr. Tu Ngoc Quang, who was accompanied by a child. Quang was the brother of an old friend of Toan's, Tu Ngoc Tỉnh from Phuc Nhac, Vietnam. Quang was willing to trade lots, giving the Vuong family lot 1, since their family was larger and it was more convenient. As a result of the move, the Vuong family's living quarters at the end of the lot was roughly five meters wide with the bed.

During the registration process, to pass the time, Toan inquired about all of the living quarters at the camp. The registrar advised Toan the Thai had to put in an area on the grounds with several rows of tents that they had had to use from time to time to handle the overflow of refugees.

Ha Huyen Vo Boulevard was the main road into the camp. Every morning at 6:00 a.m., just outside the fence in front of the main gate, the Thai venders would set up to sell all kinds of foods and other vital items. You could buy ramon noodles with an egg on top for a baht. Just about everything was for sale. Fresh or dried produce was available, as were canned foods. Vegetables, fruit, and seafoods were cheap, meat more expensive: pork loin was sixty baht for a kilogram and shrimp cost five to seven baht per kilo. Local fruit ran a few baht per kilo. Some vendors even sold clothes, materials, and watches, while others bought gold and served as money changers. The refugees were permitted to go to the outdoor market from 7:00 to 9:00 a.m. Some of the more industrious refugees made their own dishes to sell: steamed rice, soups, rolled cakes, noodles, and porridges for breakfast. There were even several shops set up inside the camp along the main road into the facility selling coffee until late at night. For a period of time, Ms. Lien, Nha-Y's sister, Hong, and Quynh Hoa prepared and sold sweet porridges and jellies, but they soon stopped since the effort to prepare it didn't make enough money to keep up with expenses. However, some small amounts of monies were starting to show up from Toan's sister in San Francisco.

Since Toan was now fully mobile again, he would walk around and study the lay of the camp. He and the whole family enjoyed having the beautiful white-sand beaches and the Gulf of Thailand. The Songkhla camp was surround by a barbed-wire fence, like Pattani, on all sides except the ocean side. The place was nice, the beach and ocean making the difference. There was an administrative sector and several residence quarters. The administrative sector consisted of two tile-roofed brick houses. The small one closest to the gate was the infirmary, where the French doctor worked. The big structure in the rear was used by the camp management and United Nations High Commission for Refugees office. This was where the delegations for third-world countries worked. Nearby were several tin-roofed houses used as classrooms, the photoshop of International Committee for Migration, the post office, and the radio station. Soon all the Vuong children were enrolled in the school, most of their time devoted to learning English. This occupied their mornings. In the afternoons they usually went to play on the beach and swim in the ocean.

When Toan's family and all those who came on the same refugee boat arrived at Songkhla, they were asked to give the name and number of the boat for a file. However, since it had not been registered, there was no name or number; the file was therefore incomplete. Toan gathered together the leaders from their refugee boat. After much debate, they selected the name KG 0054 for Kien Giang and their fifty-four members.

The day after going through the process to get their boat registered, Toan was laying in the hammock trying to reason out the conduct of the Thai police officer at the Pattani camp. As he went over the facts looking at it from the policeman's prospective, it hit him. While it was obvious he wanted paid under the table, Cham Run only knew that the second group of pirates had been driven off by the Liberian freighter and saved by the Thai Coast Guard. The police believed all fifty-four of those passengers still had money and gold. They'd never been told about the Thai fishermen-pirates.

Just before July, brother Can, nieces Bao Khanh, Bao Chau, and Huy (a nephew of Can's wife, Van) arrived at the camp. Toan was so happy Can finally made it out of Vietnam. On occasions, once they had settled into their space, they had meals together.

In the first week of July, after filling out their papers, the leaders got an appointment with the administrative office to complete their file to register their boat. With that new file in hand, the administrators could begin the registration process, including everyone's names and photographs. Also, there were some family notes about their desired designated countries and who they might live with or who might be their sponsors.

Toan's immediate family was given its own file, while the sisters, Hong and Ms. Lien, each got their own individual files. *Wonder why this process had never been offered at the Pattani refugee camp site. Was it because no one bribed Cham Run?* Clearly, this was a huge delay to get to America.

This inspired Nha-Y to write another poem:

Pattani

Gió ngập hoàng hôn đến Thái-Lan,
Pattani lạnh vắng hoang tàn.
Chuồng bò gặp lúc dừng chân tạm,
Rau cá qua ngày mừng được an!
Hành lý tiêu tan, quần mượn vợ,
Bèo mây gặp gỡ, 'họp quan' tràn...
Ô hay ba tháng sao không chuyển?
Ai biết Chằm Rùn có máu tham!

Since Toan was mobile, he got out and made new acquaintances. During the course of these conversations, he heard many stories. Some people talked about how the Thai police officers expected to be—or were—paid off in order to get out of Pattani. Passengers of several different boats filled with refugees told Toan that they had to come up with payments of four hundred baht for them to get out of Pattani, the primary staging camp.

As Toan continued to move around the Songkhla community, he met Dang Van Mach, who had also escaped Vietnam with his daughters, Thuy and Thao. They had arrived to Songkhla just a few weeks before the Vuong family. Mach was voluntarily working at the infirmary, and soon Toan and Can joined his little unofficial practice. Toan was happy but surprised that medical supplies were in more abundance than at his former hospital in Bien Hoa after the communists took over. It did not take long before he fell right back into his old doctor routine: up early each morning, quick breakfast and coffee, then a stroll through the vendor's market before reporting to the infirmary. While they still had not made it to the United States, or perhaps Australia, Songkhla was becoming a tolerable little community.

Toan was not the only one meeting people in the community. Nha-Y met several new friends. One in particular, Ms. Le Thi Y, had similar passions, as she was a poet and author.

While it was abundantly clear that living conditions were much better at Songkhla, because of the ever-growing size of the camp and the still limited funds available to Toan, he was still barely able to keep his family of nine fed.

Thursday, July 10, 1980

One afternoon, it was very windy and raining extremely hard, making the ocean and the surf quite rough. Quynh Dao, Thanh, and Quynh Trang were all bored because there was nothing to do. They kept going down to the beach to check if it looked as though it would clear up. Finally, late in the afternoon, Thanh, who had been sky-watching, saw that it was clearing. He went running in to tell Quynh Dao. This made her happy, but she did not want to go to her mother, who was already aggravated because Thanh had continuously bothered her all afternoon. Plus, Quynh Dao knew if anybody had a chance to talk her mom into going down to the beach, it would be Thanh. She said, "Would you go ask Mom?"

Thanh went running in to Nha-Y. "Can we go down to the beach? Quynh Dao said she would watch us. You don't have to worry about us."

No sooner did Thanh finish his plea than the sun was peeking through the clouds.

Nha-Y went to seek out Quynh Dao; she didn't have to go far. Nha-Y sternly looked at her. "If you are going to take Thanh, you have to take Trang, too. And don't go out beyond your knees."

Quynh Dao knew better than to say anything. She just nodded.

Within minutes, the three of them were on their way down. By the time they got to the beach it had quit raining, the wind had died down, and the sun was really breaking through the clouds. They all started playing and digging in the sand.

After a while, the tide had gone out and a sandbar had emerged at low tide about thirty meters out. Thanh wanted to play out there, and Quynh Trang was tugging on Quynh Dao to go out there, too. As they started to walk out through the hightide line of seashells and seaweed, another little boy, who had played with Thanh several days earlier, joined them on the sandbar.

The kids dug in the sand, trying to dig up bivalves, catch sideways-walking tiny crabs, and build a sandcastle without any buckets or molds—they did not care. It was just fun digging in the wet sand. The sun finally finished burning through all of the clouds, and the afternoon had turned nice. A couple of hours passed as the kids played; no one noticed that the tide was coming back in until water began gushing into one of the holes Thanh had dug earlier on the edge of the sandbar. Quynh Dao looked back toward the beach and realized the rising tide had filled in the shoal between the sandbar and the beach. Quynh Dao shouted, "Come on, kids! It's time to go! We have to get back to the beach!" She knew nobody could swim and made the same assumption about Thanh's new friend.

Thanh and Quynh Trang started to protest, but Quynh Dao was not to be messed with. They had to get to the beach fast. Quynh Dao had all of them hold hands as they started off the sandbar. Several steps in, the water was coming up fast and Quynh Dao hadn't taken but a few steps down the sandbar. She looked at her brother and sister as they continued to walk; the water was up to their shoulders. At first, Quynh Dao thought they could float and get to shore but at the edge of the shoal, the water was flowing out so hard and fast, the undertow started to take them out farther away from the dry beach.

Quynh Dao shouted, "Stop!" She put Quynh Trang on one hip and had Thanh jump on her back. She started toward the shore and saw the little boy struggling to keep his head up. She didn't even know his name but reached out grabbed him and put him on her hip opposite Quynh Trang. She shouted at the little boy. "You put your arms around me and hang on!"

Now all three were hanging on Quynh Dao, one on each hip and Thanh around her neck. Thanh stuck his legs through her arms, wrapped around her waist as best his little legs could, and grabbed a hold of her neck. Quynh Dao began to fight her way toward the beach while still struggling to retain her hold on her brother and sister. She realized she was almost carrying as much weight as she herself weighed. *I hope the buoyancy in the water helps.*

No sooner did she seem to have all the children under control, she tried to continue to walk but now the tide was coming up fast. Wind whipped the waves. Within three more steps, the water was over her head. She started hopping, and as soon as she landed she sprang back up and drew a deep breath. But she was only able to hop three more times. The shoal was getting deeper. Thanh got scared and tightened his grip on her neck, choking her out of fear. On the last two hops, she had not made it all the way above the water; she'd taken two big gulps of salt water and had no strength left in her legs to pop back up. Quynh Dao thought she was going to drown. The harder she fought, the farther out the waves pushed her and the three clinging children. Exhausted, she shouted, "We should try to float!"

Quynh Dao kept her grip on the children, but she stopped kicking and fighting. It was working until one big wave washed over them, pushing them under. With every bit of strength left in her body she jumped up out of the water one more time and saw a man at the edge of the water. She screamed at him: "Hey Mister! Please, help!"

Quynh Dao went down under the water again, taking her brother and sister under with them. She felt the grip around her neck lessen. She started to let go of her brother and sister. She was certain she was about to drown and wanted to give her brother, sister, and the little boy on her back a chance to survive.

Just then she felt a hand grab her arm and pull her up to the top of the water. She gasped for air and spit out large amounts of water. Everyone was coughing. Obviously, she was not the only one who had taken in water. The stranger, the Vietnamese man, had managed to grab and pull everyone up to the surface of the water and was struggling himself to help them to the beach.

Chapter Twenty-Four

Still in Songkhla Refugee Camp

Sunday, July 13, 1980

Over the few days since the children had nearly drowned, Nha-Y was keeping a close eye on them. While she still let them go down to the beach each day, she would accompany them and would not let them in the water. This was okay with Quynh Dao and Quynh Trang, their memory of the near-drowning experience still vivid. Thanh still wanted in the water, but not as persistently as in the past.

Since there was not much for adults to do in the Songkhla refugee camp, Toan and Nha-Y spent a significant amount of time lounging in hammocks or listening to the radio information service announcing refugees mail call. Toan fell deep into a routine, going to the infirmary, and he had just accepted this as the norm. He was beginning to get bored. Life had become boring for Nha-Y, too. About the only thing she seemed to do was prepare food. One day as she was cooking the family dinner, she emphatically inquired, "What are you doing to get us to the United States? Or Australia? Or France? Or anywhere?"

Her words gave Toan pause. He realized he had stopped driving as hard since he started volunteering at the infirmary. He gave her a peck on the cheek. "I promise, I'll start tomorrow on getting refocused on getting us to America or somewhere."

The next morning, Toan began in earnest to try to get out of the refugee camp. He spent many an afternoon engrossed in a letter-writing campaign to his various family members around the world. His focus was as it had always been, getting to the United States. His letters went to his sister Oanh and brother Canh in the United States. However, he also wrote to his sister-in-law Thuy in France, uncle Tan in Sweden, cousin Cuong in Ivory Coast, and cousin Thien in Canada.

July and August, 1980

On Sunday, July 27, 1980, several letters showed up, answering whether the family member would consider sponsoring them to come to their country. It had become obvious some of his letters never made it to the post office. While every individual he asked to mail his letters expected him to pay for postage, which was reasonable, some expected a fee for the mailing. Since he was tight on funds, he was unwilling to pay anyone a fee to handle his mail. It was a frustrating process. But once he started to get answers, everyone was pleased. Usually, they provided key information, replies from his brothers, sisters, or other relatives regarding their positions on sponsoring them. Sometimes, there was even a check or some money enclosed.

On July 31, Toan received an offer from Chinh, sister-in-law Thuy's husband, that informed him they could immigrate to France. He had checked into his Vietnamese medical license and discovered the country would easily recognize Toan's MD. Toan and Nha-Y were excited and made plans for their next move. Toan thought he would talk to the French doctor in the morning to learn as much as he could so they would make an informed decision.

The next morning, Toan went and talked to his confidante, the French doctor, at the infirmary. He guaranteed Toan could leave in one month after being interviewed by the delegation from the potential receiving country. He added, "If you still wish to go to the United States, you should know, there will be a long drawn-out wait, and once you are in country you will have to pass several difficult tests before you will be allowed to practice medicine."

When he got home that afternoon, he sat down in one of the hammocks with Nha-Y and relayed his conversation with the good French doctor. Upon finishing, he concluded, "I want to go to France."

Nha-Y listened to her husband's thoughts and his reason, then boldly replied, "My sisters and my children all want to go to the United States."

Toan continued to argue the point for a few minutes, then he compromised. In other words, he gave in. "We will focus on going to the United States."

On Monday, August 11, two months after arriving at the Songkhla refugee camp, Toan and his family were interviewed by the American delegation. Toan answered all their questions honestly except for some comments regarding whether or not he had been sent to the re-education camp and his service at Dong Nai hospital. His case had been given special attention, as refugees with relatives in the United States were currently receiving the highest priority. Toan believed he would be sponsored by sister Oanh. He came away from the interview believing his family would be settled in the United States within few months.

In November 1980, sisters Hong and Ms. Lien were informed to be ready to move to the transit camp Galang in Indonesia, in spite of their low priority. Toan was very happy for them, but he was baffled how their individual files got moved ahead of his high priority family file. As he fingered the chi gold ring in his pocket, he hoped and prayed he wouldn't have to bribe somebody at this point to get attention to his family file.

His friend, Dr. Mach, had been sent to Galang less than one month earlier. Before he left, he had requested that Toan assume all of his duties in the infirmary. Additionally, he made a larger personal request of Toan. If he should receive any letters and money from any of his friends, would he please forward it? It was a big responsibility but Toan accepted. A few days before sisters Hong and Lien were to leave, he received a letter for Mach, which contained fifty US dollars. He gave it to his sisters to take to Mach when they caught up with him in Galang.

Toan wrote letters to both Mach and his sisters; they would write back. However, the delivery service was erratic and slow. Upon receiving one letter, Toan learned that the sisters were sent to the Bataan refugee camp in the Philippines. Therefore, they had not been able to give Mach his money. This really bothered Toan because it reflected on his own integrity.

If Mach made contact with the relative and they told him about the money, Mach would assume Toan had kept it. As an example of how bad the delivery service was, it would be several months after his sisters had settled in California that Mach finally got his letter and money.

Toan loved helping people and providing them with comfort. He had a very good bedside manner. However, his volunteer time at the infirmary included some very disturbing events. Every few days, he had to examine young girls who had been raped by Thai pirates. One of the worst stories came from a young girl who'd just arrived in the Songkhla camp. All the other passengers on her boat had drowned. The girl was rescued by the pirates; Toan knew what price she would pay for her rescue. Her case was so extreme that later a volunteer doctor from the United States, Dr. Nguyet Merhert, came to personally conduct the followup examination. Her case brought home to Toan how blessed his own family's situation had been; no physical harm had come to any of the women in his family.

Besides dealing with the rape victims, Toan had another disturbing case. One day, Toan was in the infirmary doing his rounds when a construction worker came running in and asked him to come outside. The camp administration had started a construction project, digging a large hole. A young man by the name of Vo had been assigned to work in the hole. During the digging process, there was a sand slide that buried Vo. Despite Toan's repeated efforts to resuscitate the poor man once they extracted him from the hole, the poor man died of suffocation. It was another heart-breaking situation.

That evening Toan went home and talked with Nha-Y. They both believed it was taking longer than expected for his family to get transferred to the staging camp. Toan decided he would go the next day and talk with the camp chief.

The next morning, Toan went to the camp chief's office. The man in charge, Thanh, had been an ex-lieutenant colonel, and he was due to be transferred. Upon hearing Toan's full story, he appointed Toan the deputy chief for the camp. Thanh said, "This will give you better access to information and provide you with a greater voice in your own predicament." Then he added with a smile, "It will give you more chances to be in contact with the American delegates, thus you will be able to discuss your situation directly with those who can have the greatest influence in your circumstances. Who knows? It may speed up your family's departure."

Toan was able to find a replacement for his position at the infirmary.

At the beginning of December, 1980, the Thai government sent Mr. Thi to serve as the new camp chief. He happened to be a friend of cousin Thien at the Ministry of Finance. Thi was quick to get acclimated and acquainted. Shortly after Mr. Thi got situated as camp chief, he called Toan into his office. He advised him that as far as he was concerned the position Toan was currently serving was not benefitting him, as previously suggested. Thi asked, "Toan, if you are willing to resign your role as deputy chief, I'll immediately appoint you camp consultant. I think it will provide you better contacts to get transferred to the staging camp."

Toan agreed and did as requested. He became the camp consultant.

By early 1981, the Mr. Thi received his approval to be sent to Canada. This news was a crushing blow to Toan and Nha-Y. They were both very depressed, as Thi had been more help to the family than anyone else they had encountered.

A few days later, while Toan was lying in a hammock listening to the radio broadcast as they read off the names of those to being sent to the United States, it included the Vuong family. Toan leaped out of the hammock and ran in and told Nha-Y.

Lucky for him, all the children were present when he made the announcement. They all danced around their bed area. They were so excited. Finally, they were going to the United States.

Unfortunately, there would be another disappointment when they learned they were not going straight to the United States as they had hoped. They'd be joining some twenty other refugees going to a transition camp.

Since Toan had been such a fixture and done his job as camp consultant very well, several days later, the administration gave him a farewell banquet. This made Toan and his family very happy; it was a fantastic day.

Nha-Y wrote a poem:

Songkhla

Nghe em tháng sáu vào Songkhla,
Nắng ngập thuyền nhân, cát nhạt nhòa…
Lô Một người đông ồn vỡ chợ,
Hai giờ thư đến nằm đợi loa.
Anh văn trốn học lo vào bếp,
Chè thạch bán buôn lời chẳng ra!
Trại phó làm lâu lên Cố vấn,
Người đi tấp nập, ta trông nhà…

Chapter Twenty-Five

Off to Panat Nikhom then to Lumpini: Moving Pieces on the Chess Board

Saturday, January 10, 1981

Early in the morning, the group of twenty people climbed aboard the bus for the one thousand-kilometer journey from Songkhla to the connection camp at Panat Nikhom near Bangkok. They did not arrive at the camp until late that evening. In spite of fatigue, everybody was happy to get off the bus and get settled in.

All seven of the Vuong family were given a hut to themselves, but it was totally unfurnished. It had been a long time since they'd had any privacy. The others from the bus were assigned huts nearby. During the check-in process, Toan was told that early every morning a water truck would enter the camp. Each family could send one or two members with buckets, and they were rationed to two gallons of water per person for cooking and washing. Before laying down that night, Toan told the family that to save water, the children would bathe every other day. Naturally, Nha-Y, his wife, could bathe daily. That was the only decision Toan was going to make that night. When he laid down, he was more relaxed than he had been since they'd started trying to escape Vietnam. In addition, Toan had managed to save a few hundred dollars, all sent by relatives.

The next morning, Toan, Vu, and Quynh Dao went for a walk to explore the grounds. They had arrived in the dark of night, and the Panat Nikhom camp was quite large, divided into two sections separated by a barbed-wire fence. The inner section was again divided among ethnic groups, that is, the Cambodians, Laotians, Mnong, and Vietnamese. Each group occupied huts, open in front, with thatched walls, consisting of four wooden pillars arranged around an unpaved court in the middle. For the dozens of refugees, there was only one tiny, dirty bathroom for their common use. On the first morning and every morning thereafter, they were served small amounts of rice twice a day and meager amounts of food. Quynh Trang and Thanh, his growing children, requested extra fish sauce and burnt rice every time they received their meals. On the first morning, it was not available.

A couple of days after getting rested up and acclimated to the camp, Toan and Vu went to explore the outer section. It was filled with all kinds of trade; the locals owned many stores and shops, including restaurants, bars, supermarkets, and food stores that sold fresh produce like meat, fish, fruit, and vegetables. Toan assumed the close proximity to Bangkok accounted for the large variety of those markets.

On a few occasions, his family went to the outer section of the camp to eat fast foods and brought side-orders back to their hut to supplement later meals. There was no power in their hut—or any of the huts for that matter. Only candles provided light in the evening. What kept them going was knowing that they were so close to going to the United States. Nha-Y and the children often sat on the ground and played games, including cau co, a mind-reading game.

A little more than a week later, Toan heard that some of the group of twenty individuals coming from Songkhla had been selected to go to the United States, but to Toan and his family's great disappointment, they were not included.

They celebrated Tan Dau, the New Year celebration, in the Panat Nikhom transit camp. Not exactly what they had envisioned. Nha-Y purchased incense, candles, prepared foods, and fruit that she ceremonially placed on top of a few empty wooden boxes that served as alters for the offerings. This was a very difficult time for Toan and his family. They were so close to going to the United States, but their latest anticipation morphed into frustration. Everybody prayed to the high spirits and their ancestors to help them get to the United States as soon as possible. It was the second year in a row they had celebrated under not-so-pleasant conditions.

Ten more days passed before Toan and his family got the word they should prepare to leave. Everybody was overjoyed. As of that day, they had spent twenty-three days in Panat Nikhom.

Their dilemma was accurately described by Nha-Y's poem entitled:

Panat Nihkom

Tưởng rằng đi thẳng được như mơ,
Panat Nikhom học chữ ngờ!
Hiu hắt đêm đen sầu vận khổ,
Chập chờn lệ nến gọi hồn cơ.
Cách rào cơm cháy sao ngon miệng,
Đón Tết thùng cao thế tủ thờ.
Nước tắm ngày nao chia cách nhật,
Riêng Me mỗi bữa một phần xô!

Lumpini Camp

Tuesday, February 3, 1981

On the morning of February 3, Toan and his family, plus the other selected refugees, were put on a bus bound for the Lumpini camp in another location around Bangkok. The camp, quite crowded and dirty, was composed of an old house. Toan's family was given a narrow space on the floor, covered with a plastic sheet, to sleep. The arrangement was hot and very uncomfortable. The area was so small, Vu had to sleep in the hallway. In this camp, there were few prepared foods or other vendor stands. Using either the restroom or bathing could not be done with any privacy. Needless to say, Toan and his family used them with a high degree of discretion. Nha-Y and Toan's daughters could only bathe late at night.

Shortly after arriving at the camp, Toan went to the director and asked permission to go to Bangkok. The director said he would check into it.

A few days later, brother Can's family arrived at the Lumpini camp. The place was so crowded his family had to sleep in the main walkway just in front of the gate. Toan and Can found the overall situation totally unacceptable, but they were determined to keep focused on the promise of going to the United States soon.

About a week after his initial request, Toan received permission to go to Bangkok with Dung, a young man had met in Songkhla. Toan wanted to purchase some food that was not available in the camp and a T-shirt for Nha-Y. When Toan returned from shopping and checked back in, the director advised him his family would be moving again in one week.

Nha-Y composed a poem to memorialize the time of their short stay entitled:

Lumpini

Đất chật người đông, ở tạm thôi,
Lumpini mộng ngỡ lưng trời!
Nylon một tấm nằm chen chúc,
Tiền lãnh năm ngày tiêu xả hơi.
Bangkok rong chơi mua áo mới,
Galang nào biết đợi nhau rồi.
Anh em gặp gỡ tràn hi vọng,
Mơ ước bao năm tưởng tới nơi!

Tuesday, February 10, 1981

Toan and his family believed that when they arrived at the Utapao airport in Bangkok, they were headed to the United States. However, just before boarding the Thai Airline plane, they were informed they were being sent to the Galang camp in Indonesia by way of the Singapore airport. Just another disappointment in a long line of disappointments. Yet, he did everything within his power to remain calm.

They landed at the Singapore airport on a very dark night. The plane taxied to the far end of an airport terminal. When they had disembarked, a spokesman called them to gather around him. He used a megaphone and spoke in fluent Vietnamese. Their destination was Galang Two camp, which had just opened at the beginning of the year. He told them one more thing: Until that night, only one other group had been admitted to this new camp. The Galang One camp had become so overcrowded, it spawned the opening of this new camp. Toan did have one friend he knew for sure who had been sent there, the Vong family. When the spokesman finished talking, he pointed everyone toward the bus, which pulled away before everyone had taken their respective seats. After a short ride, they pulled into the harbor. The bus stopped alongside a medium-sized boat with a cabin for those to get inside if they wished. As the boat pulled away from the dock, everyone was given a box of rice and a can of chrysanthemum-flavored tea. This proved to be very calming.

Chapter Twenty-Six

Singapore

Galang Refugee Camp: Indonesia

Friday, April 10, 1981

Around 10 p.m., Toan's family was escorted to a thirty-meter motor boat. Upon boarding they were ushered by one of the crew to their own cabin room furnished with wooden benches. The crewman informed them they had a full compliment of crew to assist the passengers. Toan was both exhausted and feeling a little depressed, so he went and laid down on one of the benches.

As he lay there attempting to fall asleep, he kept repeating to himself that they were still destined for the United States. At that moment it seemed far off. Realizing he wasn't going to fall asleep fast, he opened his eyes and started looking around at his family. Some were sitting there chatting, while others were sleeping. Toan closed his eyes and flashed a quick smile again.

Toan was startled awake from a very deep sleep by voices outside the cabin door. Sitting up and wondering where he was for a second or two, he quickly remembered he was on a boat. Those voices outside the cabin were about the sunrise.

He got up and went out on the deck. After watching the gorgeous sunrise, he began searching the horizon for land. Far off there was a speck of a green island. As he was fixated on it, he realized his wife and children were on the deck with him. They watched for a few more minutes and went back to their cabins to actually brush their teeth and wash their face. *What had been a daily routine taken for granted in the past,* thought Toan, *now seemed like such a luxury.*

For the next hour, they were all like popcorn, popping back out on the deck to hold the railing and watch the far-off land, approaching fast. finally, they reached the port on the island. It was picturesque seeing the tiny fishing boats along their path. Once the boat was tied off at the dock, a sailor lowered a board and motioned in an exaggerated fashion for everyone to go ashore.

His family was greeted at the end of the dock area by an official-looking individual. He pointed everyone toward a bus sitting about fifty feet away. Toan sat down behind the bus driver. Within a short time they were traveling a narrow, paved road. Toan had a very difficult time mentally processing the bus being driven on the left side, English style. To attempt to take his mind off from the driving, he glanced around at the scenery as it slowly passed.

The bus slowed as it pulled in and traversed an inhabited camp area. Toan saw what he believed was a small hospital, some offices and stores, numerous shanty houses, and what looked like an outdoor movie theater. The bus driver leaned back toward Toan.

"That is Galang One. That camp is full, there is no more room for any residents." As the bus bounced on the road, the bus driver jostled in his seat but continued, "Because of the exploding immigration problems from both Cambodia and Vietnam, in early 1981, the HCR decided they needed to construct a new camp some ten kilometers from the old one." The bus driver pointed in the direction they were driving. "You all are the second group to be brought to Galang Two, and it already has over one hundred refugees."

The bus slowly ran on the narrow road, zig-zagging up and down through shallow hills and valleys covered with dry grass. With all the windows open, it was very dusty. Along the peaks of the hills were scarce pine trees. Still attempting to keep his mind off the bus being on the left side of the road, Toan saw thatched huts on pillars and a few tile-roofed houses. To add to his anxiety, there were times the driver had to swerve to avoid oncoming vehicles and sometimes in a curve to avoid oncoming vehicles on the very narrow road. It was quite nerve-racking, particularly near the tops of the hills where there was no berm.

Thankfully, the Vuongs arrived safely at the headquarters of Galang Two camp. The camp headquarters consisted of an administrative office and several classrooms immediately surrounding the complex in a small valley with construction on all sides. As per the usual routine that the Vuong family had gotten very accustomed to, upon exiting the bus, the first thing they had to do was check in at the reception office to fill out paperwork. At the end of the sign-in process, they were handed a rudimentary map and the registrar circled and pointed out their assigned space. As they walked toward the door to begin their hike to the living quarters, the registrar said, "With proof of residence, the markets will provide you with enough for the entire week, including rice, dry and canned foods, some vegetables. Every day, a water truck will bring water between 1:00 and 2:00 p.m. and dump it into the reservoir. Be sure to get there and get yours."

They carried their few items about one kilometer up a small hill to their assigned residence. On the walk up, they glanced at the buildings on wood pilings with tin roofs, as well as the dwellings or houses, such as they were. Between the headquarters and the apartments were a series of tin-roofed buildings on pilings, without walls, which served as a marketplace, where the locals sold food and other goods. Close by was a spacious grass field with a large single wooden wall that served as an old-style drive-in movie theater. As they approached their assigned area, in the middle was a long tin-roofed place with a water reservoir for the use of the refugees; in the rear were several rooms where they could bathe or wash their faces.

Toan and his family explored the dwelling. It was nicer than any of the places they had lived since leaving Vietnam. It had two floors. The ground floor had two parts: The front was furnished with a low, small wooden table, some stools to sit and eat meals; the rear was separated by bamboo panels with a door, the right used as a kitchen, the left as a restroom that, in spite of its small size, was large enough for his wife and daughters to each take a bath in private. There was an outside wooden staircase to the second floor that was empty and wood paneled. This was where the family set up the bedroom.

The next morning, Toan, Vu, and Quynh Dao wanted to go purchase their breakfast foods. When Toan stepped outside he glanced around to take in the view of the camp. The houses were built in different sectors over the portion of the camp he could see. Because of the hills he was unable to see the entire camp, but what he could see was built along four or five rows. Vu and Quynh Dao explored the camp's grounds on their way to the markets. They did minimal exploring that morning, yielding to their hunger. They picked up green beans, sugar, sweetened condensed milk, and some fresh fruit, then hurried back to the house. It was as good as the family had had it since they'd left Vietnam.

That evening, they learned that the forty-watt light bulb hanging from the ceiling was controlled by the camp. It turned on around 7:00 p.m. and off at 9:00 p.m. Both times it startled them because it went on and off "by itself." Simultaneously, this was when the lights on the "streets" came on until morning.

The next morning, Toan took Vu and Quynh Dao with him to find the market where they got their weekly food supply. The two children had to do all the work retrieving the heavy bags of home goods and carrying them across several hills. He also found markets that sold fresh meats, fish, and vegetables.

On Thursday, while exploring the grounds once again, Toan discovered an infirmary several kilometers from the headquarters, run by an Indonesian doctor. He went in and had a conversation with the doctor. He noticed there was an abundance of patients, more than one doctor could handle.

Within the first week, the Vuong family returned to English classes. It was a five- to six-week session taught at Galang Two camp in the buildings near the headquarters.

When it was time to pick up the next week's supply of food, they all realized that it was so plentiful, often not all rations could be consumed in the week. Once Nha-Y was comfortable with the children's safety, she permitted them to go to the markets by themselves to exchange some of their food for oranges and apples. Nha-Y and Quynh Hoa prepared the meals. This camp, unlike the others, allowed the refugees to move freely about the small island.

Toan quickly learned everybody hustled out when they heard the water truck coming. Those getting water scurried out with buckets to get enough for cooking. Some days, Vu would grab an extra bucket so that Nha-Y could bathe. Despite being on an island, fresh water was quite scarce. On the rare occasion it rained, the refugees would rush to bring out buckets to gather the rainwater.

Toan still watched the family's expenses closely to make sure there was always some money left over. They were lucky their relatives had sent them some.

After about two weeks in the camp, Toan sought out the camp administrator to request permission to do examinations on needy refugees, working alongside the young Indonesian doctor. The doctor was overwhelmed and obviously could use the assistance. Together, they only treated common ailments. The more severe cases were sent to the Galang One infirmary. When one of the doctors at Galang One went on leave, Toan was requested to assist there, as well.

It was also about that time that Toan and his family learned of other friends who were in this camp. They reacquainted themselves with Ung, a former sergeant at the Air Force Central Workshop and an old friend from Bien Hoa. They would go and visit with him every two or three days.

Soon they ran into another old friend, Anh, also from Bien Hoa, also a former sergeant at the Air Force Central workshop. On some evenings, they would all meet at his residence to play mah jong.

On rare occasions, the family would walk to Galang Three camp, which was three kilometers away and still under construction, to take baths and wash their clothes. It was on one of the construction sites Toan met the contractor, Mr. Handojo. They quickly became friends and Handojo would often come to their home to bring food and other useful goods. Toan asked, "Why are they building Galang Three, when there is still Galang Two?"

Handojo put his hands on his waist. "I don't ask, I just build. Frankly, I don't care as long as I get paid. Maybe they are trying to be proactive as so many are escaping parts of Southeast Asia. Maybe it is because they come from so many different countries here, like they're afraid they won't all get along."

Camp life was relatively easy. The Vuong family often went to the organized movie projection in the grass field near the market for the refugee entertainment, usually presented on the weekends. The family would walk sometimes as much as ten kilometers per day, and by evening they were all tired. In the evening, they could hear the cicadas buzzing, what brought back memories of summers past in Vietnam.

To recall their month-long time in Galang, Nha-Y composed the poem:

Galang

Sóng giục thuyền câu, hương gió đưa,
Đây Galang bát ngát đôi bờ.
Nhà sàn ngập nắng ôm hồn nhớ,
Ve khóc trên ngàn thương lối xưa.
Bệnh xá ngày nao chừng đổ nát?
Người xa từ độ cũng ơ hờ…
Lâu rồi trái táo nào thơm miệng?
Đồi nắng ru em tròn tuổi thơ.

Chapter Twenty-Seven

Galang Two, Singapore to California

Galang Two

Early Sunday, May 10, 1981

The Vuong family was informed by the United States Catholic Conference to prepare to go to their final destination, San Francisco, in the United States of America. Each family member was given a physical exam. Toan was also told that once they arrived in the United States, he would have to sign up with the International Commission for Migration for repayment of their airfare and other expenses.

After three months in Galang Two, they were headed for their final settlement. As soon as the exams were completed and, of course, paperwork signed, they were loaded on the bus to take them to a boat. On the bus ride, Toan met Dr. Nguyen Thi Tu, who had just escaped Vietnam, coming directly to

Indonesia. The bus ride took an hour to get back to the dock and board the boat back to Singapore. It was funny, they followed the same road back down to the dock, but it did not seem as narrow and winding back down as it did coming to the camp. As soon as they made it to the dock, they were hustled onto a motor boat to begin the trek back to Singapore. The boat ride seemed a little longer. *Was it anticipation of getting to the United States?*

Upon arrival at the transit Singapore camp, just five miles outside the large international city, the Vuong family was informed that nobody was permitted to stay at this facility more than sixty days. The camp occupied quite a spacious area with many isolated houses, most of them multistoried. They received all refugees who had been accepted for settlement from third-world countries. The Vuong family was assigned a narrow place on the floor. They were provided blankets and sheets to put on the ground to sleep. The biggest drawback was that the family had to go to a nearby building to bathe or use the restroom. Refugees received a daily allowance of Singapore $1.00 a day per person to spend on food and other expenses. As a part of their preparation to go to the United States, they were informed this was equivalent to US $0.50. They were also allowed to go outside the camp shopping every day. Once again, Nha-Y and Quynh Hoa shared in the cooking, but they did go out to eat occasionally.

Often Toan would make the bus trip from the camp into the outskirts of the large city, by himself, to purchase daily-use goods. He had been told the costs of goods in the inner city were more elaborate and more expensive, so he did not venture there.

Nha-Y wrote about the family's short time in Singapore:

Singapore

Tị nạn sang đây được cấp nhà,
Singapore trạm cuối đường hoa.
Bao lâu sương gió gian lao đủ,
Nay bỗng văn minh lịch sự hòa!
Thành phố tiêu dao cho thoả chí,
Ăn tiêu phung phí khỏi lo xa.
Người đi cười nói vui như Tết,
Tưởng sắp lên tiên hốt ngọc ngà!

After about a week in Singapore, Toan was told to get his family ready to go to the United States.

On Monday May 18, 1981, they boarded a bus to take them to the Singapore International Airport. As the bus slowly moved across the city, stopping and going due to heavy traffic and signal lights, Toan felt as though he was looking down from inside the silent coach on Singapore. He recognized several streets from back in 1969, when he had spent a month training in family planning. He continued to stare out the bus window not paying attention to his family. He knew he would likely never be in this city again. *I wonder if the Thong family is still in the area, or even alive. I enjoyed playing mah jong with them. The man drove a very fancy Peugot 403. Loved riding in that car. The city has grown up so much, bigger department stores. It is still very clean but there's still a slum area. People still hang clothes on their balcony or on wires.* He smiled when he remembered buying two toys for his young children, Quynh-Hoa and Quynh-Dao—a beautiful Italian doll and for Vu it was the noisy toy machine gun. *That was the most noisy present!*

The landing lights of the Singapore International Airport broke his trance. They were still a short distance from the airport terminal. He turned and looked at his children: The girls were chatting quietly, and Vu and Thanh were staring out the windows. They pulled up to the terminal. Toan led the children off the bus with Nha-Y shooing everyone out.

Within forty-five minutes, the ICM chartered jet was taxiing out away from the terminal. Toan glanced around at the estimated one hundred passengers on board. The pilot came on the radio and announced they were next in line for takeoff. Toan looked up and watched the stewardess hustle through the cabin to her seat at the back of the plane. As the jet lurched forward down the runway, it began to shudder as it accelerated. Everybody seemed happy when it lifted off after the long run. Toan waved his hand out the tiny window. "Goodbye, refugee camps! Goodbye, Singapore!"

Once in the air, as the jet climbed, it circled the airport then back over the city. It was gorgeous.

Within a few minutes, Toan was fixated through the tiny window at the immense ocean. Upon reaching cruising altitude, the stewardess went through the cabin, passing out drinks. He realized he had been staring out his little window for almost an hour.

He turned his attention inside the airplane. He got emotional looking at all six of his beloved family. Nha-Y and Quynh Hoa appeared to be sleeping; Vu, Quynh Dao, Quynh Trang, and Thanh were chatting while trying to take turns looking out their window or around the cabin. Feeling greatly satisfied, he leaned back, closed his eyes and fell asleep for a short time. When he awoke from his short nap, strangely, he was experiencing some mixed feelings: vaguely regretting these days living in refugee camps and feeling anxiety about what might lay ahead in his family's future. They would have to restart life in a foreign country, the United States of America. Their effort to leave had begun six long years earlier. His family had changed since his beloved South Vietnam fell to the communists. *Vanessa wasn't even a teenager,* he thought, *now she's almost a woman. Thanh was a toddler; now he's a little boy.* Toan knew the process had aged him. *Four failed escape attempts. Our quest was on the verge of fulfillment, yet the dream, which at times seemed out of reach, was about to become a reality.*

Stewardesses passed among the rows of seats. Flying against time, daytime was shorter, darkness came quicker. The jet landed at Guam for a brief period of time to refuel, then was back in the air in about an hour. The flight crew continuously announced time changes, including the date change when the airplane crossed between Guam and Hawaii, about to land at Honolulu International Airport.

Once back in the air, the sky was breaking from the sun rise, the night clouds cleared. The stewardesses passed through the cabin serving breakfast. Upon finishing his meal, he looked back outside through the small window, the sky only a slightly different shade than where it met the sea. By mid-morning, it was a clear, beautiful day.

The pilot came on the loudspeaker, "We are approaching Oakland International Airport." In an irony of world travel, they would get to relive the same date since they flew against time. *Would that I could relive other days.* The pilot continued, "The crew will be coming through the cabin to pick up. Please make sure your seat belts are buckled."

Toan looked back out the window again, he could to see the blurry land ahead of the aircraft, then saw the Golden Gate Bridge. It was so much different than approaching land on a boat. It was around 10:00 a.m. when the jet touched down on the runway at Oakland International Airport. Toan was anxious if sister Oanh would come to welcome his family.

He looked around at his family. They were all excited. They'd made it to the United States! He was excited, too, but at that moment he was reflective. He reached in his pocket then pulled his hand back holding the gold ring that Quynh Dao had placed in her mouth when confronting the pirates. He cupped it so only he could see it. He had held it back for an emergency. While there were times the situation was dire, but something positive had always come through to allow him to hold the ring back. Now it was to be saved forever; it would be their Ring of Freedom.

Now, the next adventure begins.

Epilogue

The Vuongs in America:

Where Are They Now?

Recall that on Tuesday evening March 25, 1980, Toan sat down with his family. He was risking everything he and his family had for the sake of freedom. In America, there is the saying, "Freedom isn't free." He gathered his family around and stood before them: "We are about to embark on this escape attempt, and you must understand we might not make it. Most likely we won't make it, but we are doing this as a family. None of us can swim, none of us know what's on the other side, so the odds are greatly stacked against us. One in a hundred chance of making it. But we are going to do this as a family and if we make it, you all have to make something of your lives. You have to make this effort worthwhile." That charge lay before them through all their escape attempts.

How did the family respond once they got to the United States more than a year later, on May 19, 1981?

Father: Dr. Vuong Tu Toan

The family started out on welfare and food stamps. They rented a studio apartment for $425 per month near the residence of Toan's sister Oanh. It was partly furnished with donated furniture. Two beds were placed side by side, and everyone slept on them except Vu, who used the sofa. Oanh gave the Vuong family $300 to purchase a new 19" TV set.

Toan was briefed regarding the process to get his license to practice medicine in the United States. First he had to take—and pass!—the tests of the Education Commission for Foreign Medical Graduates (ECFMG). The test consisted of three eight- to nine-hour tests on consecutive days. Toan took the ECFMG test in January of 1982, and two months later he was notified that he had passed the medical test but failed the English test.

In mid-1982, the Vuong family moved into an apartment with more space—a living room, two bedrooms, and one bathroom—in the same building as his sister Oanh. The rent was $350 a month. One bedroom was for Toan and his wife, the other bedroom was for the three girls, while a sofa bed in the living room was for Vu and Thanh.

In July of that year, Toan retook the third part, or *the patient management test*, and passed. Now he had to retake the English portion. In August, Toan took the Test of English as a Foreign Language and received a high enough score to opt out of the ECFMG English test.

Later, Toan applied for and received his Florida license from the Department of Professional Regulation; immediately, he began to send applications to many different Florida hospitals but received no favorable responses. Toan flew to Florida to look for a job but it turned out to be a wasted trip.

Still, in mid-July 1984, Toan, by himself, moved to Florida to resume his job hunting. When he landed what he thought would be a stable job, he called for Nha-Y and Quynh Dao, Quynh Trang, and Thanh to move to Spring Hill, Florida, before the Fall school year of 1985.

Between July 1984 and February 26, 1988, in order to support his family Dr. Vuong Toan held seven jobs and lived in five different cities in Florida.

On February 26, 1988, Toan was accepted into a full-time position at the Florida State Hospital in Chattahoochee, Florida. This was the largest of four psychiatric hospitals in the state and occupied a big three-story building with five wards. He was assigned to U-14, one of the two forensic units in charge of

E ward. He worked from 8:00 a.m. to 4:30 p.m., five days a week. His typical day started in the chart room reviewing the on-duty register, then came rounds with a psychologist and a nurse in the ward by 9:00 a.m. Afterwards, he joined a team meeting. In the afternoon, he reviewed charts of to-be-supervised patients then made those rounds. Before the day was over, he'd go to the library to take out psychiatric books to study.

In June, the director offered Toan a rental house on the state property; the property had been vacant for a while. Toan went to visit his family to discuss moving them to Chattahoochee.

He was doing such a good job at the facility that they added more responsibility. At the end of August, before school started and about the time his six-month probationary period ended, Toan moved his wife and Quynh Trang and Thanh to Chattahoochee and enrolled the children in a local high school.

In September, the hospital started a program that trained Toan and several other physicians in the field of psychiatry. The next month, they added training by assigning him to work in the neurology and psychiatric clinics.

At the end of 1989, Toan received some annual leave. The Vuong family went to California to see Nha-Y's sister, Hong, get married at a big family gathering.

In June 1990, Toan finished his psychiatric training and received his certificate. In the summer, Toan and his family vacationed in Canada to visit other family members.

When Toan retired in 2001, he and Nha-Y moved to New Orleans to live near Vu. Then in 2018, Toan and Nha-Y moved to Charlotte, North Carolina, to live close to Dao and Trang.

Mother: Nha-Y Pham

When Nha-Y's children started school, she also started, attending English as a Second Language (ESL) class. Previously, she'd been in an orientation class at Alemany since early 1982. However, she could not find a job. The former high school Vietnamese literature teacher, finally, was able to find work at a laundry shop owned by a Chinese individual. Later, she added a second job sewing at a private home for cash; she was paid three cents per meter of cloth lace. She had to take a bus, at twenty-five cents per ticket. However, she was not able to make more than twenty dollars in any month. Later, she was able to find employment at a photo shop, earning a little more than minimum wage.

In October 1986, due to her work experience in Spring Hill, she was able to land a job as a cashier at K-Mart with a salary between seven hundred and eight hundred dollars per month. Since Toan was out of work, she took a second job as a cashier at China Star restaurant near the K-Mart. Her hours were from 4:30 p.m.-10:30 p.m. every day. This part-time job added about five hundred dollars per month plus free suppers. Toan chauffeured the children to and from school, as well as Nha-Y between her jobs.

Nha-Y and the two children moved to Tampa in the summer of 1987. After looking for a while she was able to get on at another K-Mart.

Once her husband took his job at the Florida State Hospital, she moved to Chattahoochee, Florida, to live.

Oldest daughter: Quynh Hoa, nee Vanessa

When Vanessa (Quynh Hoa) came to the United States in May 1981, her first issue was to learn the English language. As with all the other Vuong children she enrolled in a beginner ESL class for a year during high school. She worked very hard to grasp the new language. As a result of her hard work, she began her sophomore year in high school and was placed in advanced English. When her parents moved to Florida,

Vanessa and her younger brother, Vu, decided to stay with her maternal aunt in the Bay Area.

Upon graduating high school, Vanessa enrolled in San Francisco College for two years, then transferred to San Francisco State and completed her bachelor's in accounting.

In November 1997, Vanessa married her husband, Lam. They have lived in Walnut Creek, California, since 2006 and have two children. The oldest is Kevin, fifteen years old and a junior in high school, and the youngest, Phillip, thirteen years old and an eighth grader.

Currently, Vanessa is an accountant at BevMo, a privately owned corporation selling alcoholic beverages and party supplies throughout several western states.

Oldest son: Vu Vuong

Upon the family's arrival in the San Francisco, Vu's father was able to teach them some key phrases in English before going out to accomplish the simplest tasks, such as going to the store. Immigrating to the United States was not easy nor was assimilating in America without a good grasp of the English language. Vu's aunt arranged for Mr. Adrian Leeman to come by weekly as an English tutor to spend several hours working with the family one on one and as a group. Often Vu would be the last one there working with this kind gentleman.

When his parents moved to Florida so his father could re-start his medical career, Vu and his older sister Quynh Hoa decided to stay with their maternal aunt in the San Francisco Bay Area. At this point, Vu's parents were busy trying to survive financially in the United States and he wanted to relieve some of that stress on them. However, he knew he had also been given a charge to achieve at the highest level possible academically. It made sense for him to stay in San Francisco, as he had almost finished with high school.

Not only did Mr. Leeman teach Vu English, he also taught him many things about culture, customs, traditions, and the peculiarities of the language. It was Mr. Leeman who told Vu that he was "Berkeley material" and encouraged him to apply to that university. Mr. Leeman said it would be his easiest way to med school. The man believed in Vu's abilities that paved his way into one of the premier colleges in the country. Sadly, he died shortly after Vu was accepted into the University of California at Berkeley.

On campus, Vu found pre-med difficult, but with his personal drive it was not impossible. After undergraduate studies, he was accepted in medical school at the University of California at Davis.

Vu's hardest task proved to be the application and interview process for getting a residency. The residency did not come without its own hurdles, including taking three trips by himself, to several East Coast cities in December, fighting snowstorms and frigid weather, to crime-infested inner cities with dilapidated hospitals then to rural, middle of nowhere towns that he didn't care to name or remember.

Due to his upbringing as the oldest boy and the family's escape from Vietnam, Vu was forced to be independent. This independence manifested in his first physician's assignment in New Orleans, a charming southern city. For the first time, he was separated from his family and now even from his high school and college friends. The arduous process of residency, the long hours, and, at times, the work load were overwhelming. Yet, this was his lifetime dream, taking care of patients as he had seen his father do. Soon he was making new friends in a totally different part of the United States. Vu met his new best friend, Anh Nguyen, a distant family relation, who took him in as family.

Before Anh Nguyen moved away, he introduced Vu to the future love of his life, a lovely, strong-willed lady who eventually became his wife. Vu married a couple of years after finishing his OBGYN residency at LSU. He is now the head of the Department of Family Medicine at his hospital, LSU Shreveport, plus the lead clinician of the OBGYN department, working for Ochsner Health System in southern Louisiana.

True to the American Dream in the Land of Opportunity, Vu bought a house in the suburbs, married a gorgeous and capable wife, and they have two well-behaved children. The older one, Christopher, started college this fall at Tulane University, one of the best colleges in the country. And the younger one, Matthew, is doing very well as a sophomore at Jesuit High School, one of the best high schools in the city.

In the end, Vu's acknowledges the sacrifices his parents made, plus their foresight m instilling him with a strong work ethic and knowledge of the value of self-reliance and perseverance. He will always remember Mr. Leeman, the man—the *friend*—who guided him through the transition into American society and believed in his potential early on. Also, there was his maternal aunt, who became his second mother, nurturing him through his last year of high school and throughout college. Vu's tribute to his parents was his achievement, gained on the backs of their sacrifices.

Middle child: Quynh Dao Vuong

In the fall of 1982, Dao started in the eighth grade at George Washington High School in San Francisco. She was inhibited by her English deficiency, despite watching cartoons and TV sitcoms to build her skills. Dao also enrolled in an ESL class taught by a Chinese teacher who often explained questions in Mandarin, which hardly improved her language skills. The most helpful of all was a Mr. Lynn, a Catholic church volunteer, who provided private lessons for all the family. For all his work, Nha-Y had to have a big pot of coffee for Mr. Lynn to drink.

As Dao quickly made up her language deficiency, and she was soon in regular classes, which accelerated her learning. However, getting into the mainstream student body did not keep her from racism and bullying. Dao was also very athletic she made the cross country and gymnastic teams.

Throughout most of Dao's junior year, now in Florida attending Frank W. Springstead High School, she was the only Vietnamese student; there was only one other Asian student in the school. She was accepted into the student body much better than she had been in San Francisco. She took AP classes and was in the English Honor Society and the German Club. Dao graduated class valedictorian.

When her parents and Quynh Trang and Tom moved to Stuart, Florida, Dao wanted to stay in Tampa since she was just three months from starting college. Her English teacher, Mrs. Long from high school put her up until she enrolled. Dao started the fall semester at the University of South Florida with an academic scholarship while the balance of her expenses were paid by Pell and other grants. Her major was biology and pre-med. Upon completing her undergraduate work, she was accepted into the med school at South Florida.

As soon as Dao completed med school, she was matched to the OBGYN Residency program at the University of Florida, where she was accepted for residency from 1994 to 1998.

When Dao started at the University of South Florida, she met her future husband, Bill McDaviit, who was an adjunct professor and taught karate courses in the physical education department. She became totally obsessed with Shotokan karate, raising to the level of Second Dan. Her husband, a Fifth Dan, continues to instruct today, though Dao had to stop practicing due to a knee that never fully recovered after surgery. Bill and Dao started dating her junior year of college and they were married about the time she graduated from her residency.

Upon completing her residency, Dao moved to Charlotte, North Carolina, in 1998 and joined a growing private practice group in the UNC area of Charlotte. In 2004, four members—Lisa Gorsuch, Ehab Sharawy, Holly Stevens, and Dao—broke away to join Novant Health. This team very quickly achieved success and grew rapidly into one of the top OBGYN practices in the area. In March 2019, Dao and many in the Novant practice moved to join a Holston Medical Group.

Since 2006, Dao has consistently been on the list Best Doctors, a group nominated annually by peers of the best doctors in communities throughout the country.

Dao and her husband, Bill, have three daughters; the oldest is fifteen and twins, age twelve. The children are in the eleventh and seventh grades at Community School of Davidson. The oldest one has told her parents she wants to be an OBGYN.

Youngest daughter: Quynh Trang Vuong

Upon first arriving in San Francisco, Trang remembers her family having to accept government assistance including Medicaid and Welfare, with free school lunches and free glasses. Their clothes were from the Salvation Army, and they sported three-dollar sneakers and faux Member's Only jackets. Trang knew her family had little, but they were loved and free to fulfill their dreams. All seven of the Vuong family lived in a studio not much more than twenty-five by twenty-five. Trang remembered her sisters sleeping in the closet. They were not well accepted in the community, complete with dirty stares and disapproving gestures as they peeled their food stamps out of those booklets. It was not uncommon for them to go to bed hungry and scared many nights.

In 1982, Trang started in fifth grade in San Francisco. Trang was very concerned about learning English, and the culture of the United States terrified her. She enrolled in ESL when she started 5th grade and heard or witnessed so many stories of miscommunication, she was afraid to raise her hand in class. In addition, she was intimidated by the other students.

Because of her father's difficulties finding a job since he was not a board-certified physician in the United States, the family along with the youngest children had to move multiple times. Naturally, every time their father moved, Trang's mother, a former high school teacher, always endeavored to find two jobs to support the family. Trang went to two different middle schools and four different high schools. Making friends was difficult, particularly because she was Vietnamese. Despite the adverse conditions, Trang went on to be the salutatorian of her high school.

She started her undergraduate studies at the University of Florida. Trang was concerned about applying to med school, out of fear of how her parents—particularly, her father—would view it due to the financial demands. Because of her excellent academics, she received early admission to med school at the University of Florida. To attempt to control the stress on her parents, she completed her undergraduate and medical school in seven years instead of eight.

Trang met her future husband, Jerry, while at the University of Florida. They were sparring partners at the school's karate club. Jerry took the critical RN nurse path in order to support Trang throughout her medical school and residency years.

After residency, they moved with their six-month-old son, Tyler, to Morristown, Tennessee, a very small town near Knoxville where patients would often bring their moonshine, bushels of corn, homemade apple butter, and so on as payment. It was and still is a pinnacle of southern hospitality. She maintains contact with some of those patients yet today, but both she and her husband wanted to move back to Florida for family reasons. When that position did not work out, she moved to Charlotte, North Carolina, got an interview and accepted a spot at Novant Urgent Care, where she has been since 2006.

The most important thing Trang's parents taught her was to achieve her dreams, dreams not possible had she stayed in Vietnam. She went on to become double board certified in both internal medicine and pediatrics. Growing up in Vietnam and watching her dad taking care of patients allowed her to see firsthand how people viewed him and the medical profession. She saw distressed parents clinging to their sick child, praying and hoping that he would have the answer and the cure. Nine out of ten times, he would. She admired her father so much, which started her interest in medicine.

Trang whole-heartedly believed that her success as a good doctor and a decent human being came from experiencing her own hardships. Being poor and struggling taught her that to balance food and money, you have to have been sick and scared. Their second daughter was born with a hole in her heart, which required heart medications for heart failure, tube feeding, multiple medical specialists. One should be humble and always do the right thing.

The youngest boy: Thanh (Tom) Vuong:

Tom's story of coming to the United States is unusual because he was so young when the Vuong family began their escape. While in Songkhla, Thailand, he remembered singing "London Bridge is for Linda" because it was the name of the Peace Corp teacher who was teaching them English. He remembered mouthing the pledge to the flag. In his early childhood in Vietnam, he remembered being told he was below average in one of his classes, ranked fiftieth out of sixty students. Each of the children had to put some money in to purchase prizes; he won a plastic canteen that wasn't worth the money he contributed.

Upon arriving in San Francisco, like his brothers and sisters he was placed in an ESL class for the first few years. The class had mostly Mexican and Chinese kids in it, and weirdly, they were learning Spanish songs. Things changed drastically once he was in first grade because competition was less stiff than Vietnam. His teacher dubbed him The Human Calculator based on what he'd learned from his siblings while hiding out at his maternal grandfather's and during the various refugee camps. This nickname stuck all through secondary schooling. Through secondary education in the United States, he did not need to push himself, yet still excelled, earning good grades due to his parents' expectations. While in high school, he also enrolled in Tallahassee Community College to earn college credits. He was valedictorian of his senior class and received a full scholarship to the University of Florida. He graduated cum laude from the university with a bachelor of science in marketing in 1997.

All through school, Tom believed he was destined to be a doctor because it's just the Vuong and Vietnamese way, as that occupation was held in such high regard. However, once he was in high school, due to his unbelievable math skills, he found himself drawn to the video game industry. Tom was quite candid about this, which caused a rift with his parents, his father in particular.

Upon graduating from college, Tom earned his real estate license and started selling timeshares. While it was not what he wanted out of his career, he needed a job and income, not wishing to take anything more from society. Then an opportunity to enter the gaming industry came along—testing his favorite game, NCAA Football for PlayStation. Then an additional opportunity presented itself: EA Sports was looking to move production to Florida, which created permanent positions.

Tom was transferred to work on Madden and NCAA football for the next eight years, then promoted one more time to associate producer. While at EA Sports, he had witnessed growth from fifty to over seven hundred employees, when he decided to move on. In 2007, Tom had kept his foot in the real estate business while he worked at EA Sport, then he joined a local real estate investment club. His move coincided with the peak of the real estate market just in time to ride it down in the crash. In order to fight his way through those tough times, Tom ended up as an entrepreneur, "flipping houses," plus holding back a few for his own rental properties and starting a fledgling title company. Surprisingly, he still does math the way he learned to in Vietnam.

Living in Chattahoochee, Florida, Tom married his high school sweetheart, Cherie Jones. They met in eighth grade and started dating when he was a junior in high school. They live in Orlando, Florida, and have two well-adjusted happy boys, J. J., thirteen, and Kai, seven.

Over the past few years, Tom and his family have had many amazing experiences traveling the world. Over the years, counting living in Vietnam, Tom has lived in nine different cities. The moving around from his early childhood until now has made him comfortable with change, almost embracing it. Tom's philosophy: *Life is fluid and what we have today, we may not have tomorrow. We can only live for today and enjoy the moment. Success is knowing what makes you happy and being driven enough to pursue it, regardless.*

Tom was a momma's boy growing up. His most influential sibling was the super-driven Dao. While she was in high school training for the cross-country team, she would get Tom up to go jogging with her in the early morning hours. Trang was the closest in age; they were bonded growing up. It was her task to keep Tom alive. As an adult, Tom has grown closer to Vanessa because of her spirit and sense of humor. Vu helped him during a rough time in college in a very surprising way—though he really did not appreciate it at the time. Tom told Vu he wished his dad was more of like his friends' dads, supportive and communicative. Of course, Vu replied that, though their dad wasn't perfect, he was pretty damn close. It caught him off guard but gave him a new perspective.

Since Tom was the youngest of the five children, he was often the subject of his siblings' and their friends' attention. In order to join them, Tom had to develop thick skin and a sense of humor. Besides the normal verbal and physical abuse, occasionally he was asked to do outlandish stuff for attention: One day, Vu and his friends dared him to kiss a cat's butt. Did Tom do it? Of course.

Then there were the times Dao and Trang would tie him up and torture him to spill secrets. The humor and high jinx was not limited to his siblings and their friends. One funny situation got Dao, Trang, and Tom in trouble with their dad. They were splashing in the cistern that was used to flush the toilet. Yes, it was considered dirty and had rats running around. Unbeknownst to the kids, Tom's dad came home early one day to bring Tom a new plastic chicken-riding toy to ride around on. The three children tried to hide and be quiet in that nasty pool because they didn't want to be found where they weren't supposed to be. Their father was calling for Tom and the others. However, they had been playing with some toy soldiers and when the soldiers started floating away, they all started laughing. Needless to say, all three of them got "whoopins" that day. That was the late 1970s, after all.

The first things that stand out about these mini biographies are the additional sacrifices Toan made. He could have put his foot down in the Songkhla refugee camp and said, "I want to go to

France, where I can immediately resume practicing medicine. That is the end, no more debate." But he did not. He did what he believed would be best for his children.

In summary, after the Vuong family arrived in the United States, the father and mother continued to set the table with their sacrifice so all of their children could feast on the bounties of a new life. As Toan said on the night before they started their successful escape from the communists of Vietnam: "We are about to embark on this escape attempt, and you must understand we might not make it. Most likely we won't make it, but we are doing this as a family. None of us can swim, none of us know what's on the other side, so the odds are greatly stacked against us. One in a hundred chance of making it. But we are going to do this as a family and if we make it, you all have to make something of your lives. You have to make this effort worthwhile."

List of Names

Immediate Family

- Toan Tu Vuong – Father – Physician
- Nha-Y Pham – Mother - High School teacher and poet
- Quynh-Hoa – Vanessa (oldest daughter)
- Anh Vu – (next, oldest son)
- Quynh Dao – Dao
- Quynh Trang - Trang
- Thanh - Tom

Toan's brothers and sisters

- Toan – oldest son
- Minh – oldest sister
- Oanh – older sister
- Kien – older brother
- Bich – younger sister

- Can – younger brother – worked at the lab at the hospital pharmacy
- Canh – youngest brother

Toan's Nephews

- Anh – older Oanh's son
- Ai – Minh's son
- Vu Thin – cousin who lived in the U.S.
- Van – Can's wife
- Bao Khanh – Can's older daughter
- Bao Chau– Can's younger dauther
- Huy Can's wife, nephew of Van

Maternal Grandparents

- Judge Pham Gia He – Grandfather
- Bao – Nguyen Thien Bao - Grandmother

Nha-Y's brothers and sisters

- Nha-Y – oldest daughter
- Chinh – sister
- Thuy – sister

- Thu – brother
- Huong – brother
- Trong – brother
- Hong – sister
- Cat – brother
- Oanh - sister
- Phuong – sister

Vuong extended family

- Ms. Lien – family friend, Hong's friend

Vietnam – Hospital personnel

- Dr. Tran Van Duc - Bien Hoa hospital's chief surgeon
- Dr. Nghiem Xuan Tho – Bien Hoa hospital director and chief of the Bien Hoa Health
- Dr. Nguyen Thanh Phuoc – New Bien Hoa hospital director
- Vu Nguyen Bich – hospital staff
- Trinh Dinh Tri – hospital staff
- Dr. Truong Minh Cac - director-general of all hospitals
- Nguyen Chi Nhieu - bureau chief of Health all hospitals

- Dr. Nguyen ThI Thanh – aka Sister Hai Thanh – 1st director hospital after communist
- Dr. Nguyen Thanh Tung – doctor at the hospital
- Dr. Kham – doctor at the hospital
- Dr. Nguyen Kim Bon – aka Hai Bon – new hospital director
- Dr. Tu Mui – hospital doctor
- Dr. Khoi – hospital doctor
- Mr. Cay – directory of the pharmacy
- Dr. Hoang Minh Mau – gastroenterologist

Vietnam – Escape and refugee camp people

- Ms. Tam – Associate of Xoi
- Xoi – boat owner
- Le To Nga – Ms. Nga - Nurse at Bien Hoa hospital
- Tu Minh – Ms. Nga's husband
- Ms. Nam – Vuong's maid in South Vietnam
- Mr. Chin – boat owner
- Mr. Phat – boat owner
- Mr. Ly – associate with Mr. Phat
- Mr. Luong – Chinese boat Captain/owner
- Pilot Son – Big Boat pilot

- Sum – Big Boat passenger and repairman
- Hung – Big Boat passenger and possible owner of the boat
- Mr. Nhon – passenger on the Big Boat
- Ms. Tham Man – a neighbor of the Judge
- Ms. Lien – another lady by the same name from Bien Hoa
- Hop family – from same refugee boat as Vuong family
- Quynh Giao/Ki Keo – Hop family member
- Cham Run – Local Thai police officer
- Mr. Thinh – from the Ca Mau refugee boat
- Mrs. Tra – from the Ca Mau refugee boat
- Dr. Tu Ngoc Quang – another refugee in the Songkhla camp
- Dang Van Mạch – a volunteer at the Songkhla infirmary
- Dr. Nguyet Merhert – a volunteer United States doctor in Songkhla refugee camp
- Ms. Le Thị Y – refugee in the Songkhla camp, poet/author friend of Nha-Y
- Thanh – Songkhla refugee camp chief, former South Vietnamese Colonel
- Mr. Thi - Songkhla refugee camp new chief
- Dung – a refugee in the Songkhla camp and Lumpini camp

- Handojo – Galang Two and Galang Three construction contractor
- Dr. Nguyen Thi Tu – refugee in Indonesia

<u>Vietnam – Diplomates and Elites</u>

- South Vietnam President Nguyen Van Thieu
- South Vietnam Vice President/President Tran Van Huong
- General/President Duong Van Minh "Big Minh"
- Prime Minister Vu Van Mau
- Le Duan – Leader of the Vietnamese Communist party
- President Thang – President of the unified communist Vietnam
- Kriangsak - Prime Minister of Thailand

Made in the USA
Middletown, DE
28 November 2019

79504514R00212